Titles in this series:

1. *The Sahel: ecological approaches to land use*

2. *Mediterranean forests and maquis: ecology, conservation and management*

3. *Human population problems in the biosphere: some research strategies and designs*

4. *Dynamic changes in terrestrial ecosystems: patterns of change, techniques for study and applications to management*

5. *Guidelines for field studies in environmental perception*

6. *Development of arid and semi-arid lands: obstacles and prospects*

7. *Map of the world distribution of arid lands*

8. *Environmental effects of arid land irrigation in developing countries*

9. *Management of natural resources in Africa: traditional strategies and modern decision-making*

Management of natural resources in Africa: traditional strategies and modern decision-making

unesco

Launched by Unesco in 1970, the intergovernmental Programme on Man and the Biosphere (MAB) aims to develop within the natural and social sciences a basis for the rational use and conservation of the resources of the biosphere and for the improvement of the relationship between man and the environment. To achieve these objectives, the MAB Programme has adopted an integrated ecological approach for its research and training activities, centred around fourteen major international themes and designed for the solution of concrete management problems in the different types of ecosystems.

Published in 1978 by the United Nations
Educational, Scientific and Cultural Organization
7 Place de Fontenoy, 75700 Paris
Printed by Union Typographique,
Villeneuve-Saint-Georges

ISBN 92-3-101587-7
Aménagement des Ressources Naturelles en Afrique :
Stratégies Traditionnelles et Prise de Décision Moderne
92-3-201587-0

Printed by Etienne Julien, Paris

Preface

The first MAB Technical Note was entitled *The Sahel: ecological approaches to land use.* Without being a comprehensive study, this Technical Note dealt with those aspects which, both in the natural and human sciences, are of special importance and interest for the development of the Sahel. Indeed, this region more than any other needs intelligent applications of research results, as well as the transfer - with all due caution - of scientific knowledge obtained in bioclimatically comparable zones. Care was taken, however, to emphasize that this application and transfer of knowledge, to satisfy the needs of human societies, should take into account their particular problems and behavioural characteristics. It was also indicated that the application of such knowledge to regional land management and the rational use of natural resources was conditioned by decisions based on social and political considerations.

What remained to be done was to analyse the decision-making process, especially within State organizations concerned with land management, and to examine the relationships between this process and the societies' traditional strategies. Analysis of the differences and conflicts between these two types of procedures also needed to be made, as well as consideration of how they could eventually complement each other or where compromises would be necessary.

This is why Unesco, within the framework of the Man and Biosphere (MAB) Programme, in co-operation with the United Nations Environment Programme (UNEP) and with the help of the Institut du développement économique et de planification en Afrique (IDEP) (Institute for Economic Development and Planning in Africa) organized a seminar in Dakar from 13 to 28 January 1975 for decision-makers involved with the management of natural resources in West Africa. The twenty-three participants in this seminar came from ten West African countries and represented a wide range of disciplines concerned with resource development. Using a variety of examples, this seminar indicated how management and development decisions have a great many implications, emphasized the environmental consequences of such decisions, and, even more important, considered the reactions and attitudes of the human societies concerned with these projects. The modern decision-making process needed to be examined critically in order to take fully into account the impact of decisions on the environment and on human group behaviour. Indeed, rational and integrated management of natural resources cannot ignore the environmental impact of development projects, nor the values which traditional societies associate with their methods of natural resource utilization.

For these reasons, the Dakar Seminar was included among the activities of the Man and Biosphere (MAB) Programme in Africa, along with several integrated projects for managing forest and range resources currently underway in various biogeographical zones. The fact that this meeting took place shows Unesco's and UNEP's concern for associating decision-makers with studies on the ecosystems involved in development projects, as well as with examination of the consequences of development decisions on these ecosystems. Development decisions must be seen within the particular ecological context, so as to give due consideration to the potential of that environment and to ensure that these decisions respond to the needs of human societies.

This MAB Technical Note, while echoing the discussions of the Dakar Seminar and the analysis of concrete situations examined during organized visits to the Senegal delta and the Ferlo animal-raising areas, includes several examples of traditional strategies and of projects resulting from modern decision-making. These examples are taken from the Western and Central African geographical area covering several zones, whose classical division into the North Sudan-Sahel, South-Sahel, forest and preforest zones has been respected.

The general meaning of the word 'strategy' is to deploy the means available in order to obtain an optimum result. In dealing with strategies concerning natural resources, there is a problem with respect to space in that more than one strategy can be applied to a given area. In modern Africa, as in traditional Africa, there are many examples of groups of people who share the same space, each group applying its own strategy to the same stretch of land. These strategies may compete or complement each other. The examples taken from the three major biogeographic zones of Western and Central Africa are representative in this respect; they constitute the three chapters of this Technical Note.

Unesco and UNEP wish to express their gratitude to the six authors of these three chapters for their valuable contributions, as well as to the participants of the Dakar Seminar whose interventions helped to foster a better understanding of specific situations in the countries concerned. The opinions expressed in this publication do not necessarily correspond to those of Unesco or of UNEP.

Contents

Introduction

The ecosystem concept can be used to situate the use of natural resources in the broad framework of the interrelationships between living organisms and the physical environment, to study the effect of these interrelationships on the functioning of the different components of the system, and to identify the imbalances which can influence to a greater or lesser extent the availability of resources to human societies. Nevertheless, this concept must be used with caution in studying human societies, as they are, given their distinct cultural character, partially independent from the natural environment. Decision-makers must be aware of the fact that the interaction between the natural environment and human societies and civilizations is not always governed by the same rational and objective principles which apply to the interrelationships between the components of the natural system itself. Societies will not necessarily 'adapt' to changes in the natural environment according to a general predictable model. This relative independence of man with respect to the natural environment is a crucial factor to be taken into account by decision-makers. For this reason, it is useful to make a distinction between traditional strategies and modern decision-making in the use and management of natural resources.

Is the term 'strategy' an appropriate one in this context, as it is a military term used to mean the art of planning a campaign and leading an army? A strategy is used to attain a specific objective; but is there such a definitive objective in human society? All societies must of course feed themselves and procreate to survive. But human 'strategies' would be notably monotonous if this were their only purpose. What distinguishes human behaviour and justifies the use of the concept of strategy is that there are specific cultural values which each society associates with its survival, to the extent that survival itself can sometimes be jeopardized to defend these values. In one society, it may be the safeguarding of a high degree of individual freedom that is considered most important; in another, the maintenance of a large area of land, as a means of avoiding domination or control by neighbouring societies; in still another, the conserving of certain cultural values shared by the group. But although each society holds one value above all others, is not the idea of collective strategy simply a theoretical abstraction? Does not each individual behave differently and is not the strategy of a group in fact just the sum of more or less contradictory and always diverse individual behaviour? In reality, most traditional societies exert sufficient restraint on their members so that their behaviour is, if not identical, at least very similar. As very few societies allow complete freedom of behaviour, the notion of collective strategy can be considered a valid one.

The existence of a collective strategy based on a dominant value implies that there is an internal consistency among the different activities and behavioural patterns of a group. Just as a military strategy integrates the tactics of each weapon, a traditional strategy integrates demographic, productive, social, religious, political, artistic, etc., aspects of a society. This internal consistency is often neglected during the decision-making process. Decisions are made concerning demography, production techniques, or the attribution of space, without first evaluating the adaptations, sometimes traumatic, which must take place in the behaviour of the group. There is also insufficient awareness of the extent to which a change in one aspect of group behaviour affects the others. Thus the notion of strategy can be useful for decision-makers in that it highlights the relationships between the different behavioural practices of a traditional group.

The concept of traditional strategy is therefore a viable one, although there are some difficulties involved in clearly defining it. In attempting to identify the main value behind the strategy of a group, the research worker can find himself touching on the controversial subject of social psychology. In analysing a collective strategy, there is always the risk of overgeneralization and of overlooking many types of family or individual behaviour. In seeking the internal consistency among the diverse practices of the group and in trying to show how one is rational as compared to another, the overriding concern is to find evidence of a stable equilibrium which in reality only very rarely exists. The various practices are in fact often conflicting, or even competitive. The study of traditional strategies is undoubtedly a worthwhile exercise, but one which involves a certain amount of risk.

The study of the decision-making process also involves certain difficulties and risks. To begin with, relevant information is difficult to collect and is rarely comprehensive. Of the many international, regional or national justifications for a development project, it is usually those which can be discussed in economic terms which are mentioned; the political reasons, local influences and foreign interests are not clearly exposed. In addition, decision-making does not take fully into account the views of local populations; only in exceptional cases are technical and economic studies preceded by an opinion survey. Files are full of information which can be used to justify the project, but do not include mention of the unknown, poorly understood or hazardous factors. When a development project has been completed, it is very rarely followed by a parallel study to evaluate the consequences. Problems in obtaining information on the evolution of a project will be magnified if the project encounters obstacles or fails altogether. There are few publications which analyse the reasons for failure, although fortunately such studies have been made for several large-scale agricultural projects in tropical Africa: the Plan des arachides (Ground-nut Scheme) and the Nigeria Agricultural Project. The regional impacts of development projects are not usually studied. For example, what changes occur in living conditions? What is the impact on the country's balance of trade? What are the effects on the natural environment of the region, which extends far beyond the immediate limits of the project? The difficulties in thoroughly analysing a development project are apparent, a practice which is, moreover, rarely carried out, in spite of the fact that it can be extremely useful and can contribute to making development policies more effective.

Traditional strategies, modern decision-making and management of natural resources in the Sudan-Sahel

J. Gallais and A.H. Sidikou

I. INTRODUCTION

In Africa, the Sudan-Sahel zone, as limited by the 300 and 600 mm isohyets, spreads from the Atlantic to the Nile across an average of 2° latitude: 16,30°-15° in Senegal, 16°-14° in the Niger Basin, 14°-12° in the Nile Basin. The expression 'Sudan-Sahel' connotes a juxtaposition of regions, a transition zone between the Sudan and Sahel zones. Richard-Molard (1949) distinguishes both a North and South Sudan zone and a North and South Sahel zone. Aubréville (1950) identifies a Sudan-Sahel climate between 400 and 1,000 mm, which takes in Richard-Molard's Sudan zone by overlapping it slightly to the North. Toupet (1966) emphasizes the transitory nature of the environment of the Assaba Mountains in Mauritania, which lie between isohyets 500 and 300 mm.

An identical problem arises with the human environment and civilizations of this area. Is it a region of transition, of diversity, of disparate influences? Or is it the homeland of a civilization shaped by the long years of history, falling under the influence of outside forces to a greater or lesser extent, and therefore appearing to vascillate between Saharan pastoralism and black farming communities, while always conserving a certain dynamism and a distinct cultural identity?

The civilization of the Sudan-Sahel is agricultural and pastoral in nature. Sudan dry-farming is carried out with its short-cycle varieties of millet and sorghum adapted to drought and the brief two to three-month rainy season. Extensive stock-raising is possible up to the limits of the tsetse fly-infested zones. Ethno-botanical articles (Portères 1950) have shown that this area contains the hearths of millet (*Pennesitum*) cultivation and of African rice (*Oryza glaberrima*) domestication in the interior Niger Delta. Rain-fed agriculture is marginal. Yields are poor, 300 to 600 kg/ha of millet per year of average rainfall, falling to zero in drought years which occur every five to ten years. Nevertheless, this type of agriculture makes maximum use of rainfall, as there are sandy soils with good water-retaining properties originating as ancient ergs deposited during the Quaternary dry periods: Cayor in Senegal; Ségou and Niafounké in Mali; Djermaganda in Niger; North Nigeria; Kanem in Chad; Qoz, Kordofan and Darfour in Sudan. In the fluvio-lacustrine washes or inland deltas of the Niger, Lake Chad or the Nile, there are rice paddyfields and other non-systematic flood-retreat cropping which are at the same time characteristic of this zone and extremely original in their adaptation to the environment.

It is the same for stock-raising, which cannot be considered as a simple extension of Sahara-Sahel pastoralism. This area contains one of the largest African stock-raising regions, where cattle, mainly zebus, are raised. The association of the two activities implies the existence of original means for spatial and social organization. Indeed these activities are very well integrated at Kanem in the Sérèr country at the edge of the Niger interior delta. It is probable that this dual-purpose economy was far more widespread and took a more sedentary form before the exertion of Foulani and Twareg influences from the end of the 18th century.

Trading is also practised. Although regional products are not sufficiently abundant to be sold in large quantities (with the exception of a few small-scale handicrafts and cattle), it was the geographical position of this zone which provided the basis for the development of commercial bodies dealing with the exportation of gold produced in the Upper Niger and linked to the Mediterranean world during the Greek and Roman Empires as well as the Middle Ages. Products from the Sahara (salt) or North Africa (leather, arms, horses, textiles) and products from the forests of Guinea or Central

Unesco, 1978. *Management of natural resources in Africa: traditional strategies and modern decision-making.* (MAB Technical Notes 9).

Africa (ivory, perfumes, cola) were exchanged at trading posts which were located at various points along the same latitude from Upper Senegal to Kanem according to the changes in the North African openings to the West and East. By differentiating the regional social structures, by favouring certain tribal chiefs, by giving these chiefs a means of religious domination and external support through Islam, this trading economy is at the origin of the so-called Sudanese states: the Medieval empire of Ghana, Mali, Songhai and Bornou. The Foulani were often the continuators of these empires, where their influence was very widespread; they exert even today a unifying effect on this zone.

Finally, compared to neighbouring regions, the Sudan-Sahel zone is unquestionably an area where river valleys have provided the concrete bases for settlement and economic development. These allogenic rivers (Rivers Senegal, Niger, Lagone, Nile) flow northwards to the great Sahara basins. Their waters are highly prone to inland drainage. The seasonal floods are held back by ancient ergs and form large fluvio-lacustrine washes, whose agricultural rôle has already been emphasized. In this area the rivers and interior delta need not be avoided as they are not disease-ridden as is the case further South where they harbour onchocerciasis and sleeping sickness. North-South trade has largely exploited the possibilities of traditional navigation and the riverbanks have become the basis of one of the rare urban civilizations of black Africa. The rivers, marshes and lakes have also been exploited for their fish. In this latitude where drought lasts for nine months of the year, the washes provide valuable pastures after the retreat of the flood waters. Thus the regional pastoral societies have settled there, and every season this area attracts herdsmen with their animals from the hinterland.

These advantages explain that these great rivers became the geographical bases for the most powerful, most open and most historically important of human organizations: the Fouta-Toro Empire of the River Senegal; the Empire of Mali, Songhai and Macina of the Niger; the Nubian Empire of Senaar of the Nile. The Foulani influences of the 19th century which spread from the Atlantic to North Nigeria profoundly altered the development and the present situation of the great alluvial valleys. Those of the West, the Senegal and the upper reach of the Niger to Timbukto, were dominated by the Foulani, and their economy and spatial structures were greatly changed by the pastoral way of life. Further East around Lake Chad, the Foulani influence petered out and, apart from the plains of North Cameroun, the peasant population conserved their well-established agricultural organizations. These also remained without change on the banks of the Nile.

The Sudan-Sahel zone is therefore clearly distinguished by its high level of agriculture and pastoralism, its widespread tradition of trade and the economic and historical importance of the river valleys. Therefore it is not a transition zone but a geographical area with a distinct original character that lies between the North Sahel totally devoted to pastoralism and the agricultural civilizations of the Sudan zone. Climatic changes and historical events can alter these frontiers, but the zone has a true identity on the basis of which traditional strategies were developed, a fact often ignored in modern decision-making. Whether in the Southern agricultural regions or the Northern pastoral regions, decisions and plans for development are made for the Sudan-Sahel zone as if it were a possible extension of these areas. Ignorance of the particular characteristics of Sudan-Sahel ecosystems can mean that modern strategies are simplistic and ill-adapted, or, in other words, useless and sometimes dangerous.

II. TRADITIONAL STRATEGIES

THE ZARMA AGRICULTURALISTS

The study of Zarmaganda, or the country of the Zarma people, in Niger (Sidikou 1974) provides an example of the use of a traditional strategy in a typical Sahel zone. Zarmaganda is situated immediately to the East of the River Niger between latitudes 14° and 15°. It is a low-lying plateau where laterite alternates with the sands of the ancient ergs and the heavier soils of fossil valleys. Average rainfall varies between 300 and 550 mm (450 mm rain in 30 days at Kossi Tondi village whose records give useful references). As the conditions are marginal for rain-fed millet cultivation, yields can easily fall with a poor distribution of rainfall: a drought of 10 to 15 days after seeding will prevent germination; a dry September, or on the other hand, a very wet September will hinder ear formation and the grain will be small.

The Zarma peasant tends to adapt to this situation by firstly seeding very sparsely, to be repeated if the first seed fails. This means that he prepares several fields which he sows at intervals of a few weeks, following the pattern of the first rains. He also uses various varieties of millet with different qualities: *m'bouga*, a quick growing variety (60 to 70 days) useful in times of shortages; *hanikirey* of average growth cycle (90 to 100 days); and *darankobé*, also of average growth cycle and especially adapted to dune soils; *somno*, a slow-growing variety (120 days) which withstands drought and can be weeded later in the season. The use of these varieties with their different attributes, and the organization of work (seeding and weeding) throughout the season make it possible to guard against a hazardous rainfall pattern.

The Zarma peasant fears locusts as much as or even more than drought; the two risks are often, moreover, encountered together. His neighbour, the Kado peasant of Anzourou, falls back upon ritual practices: the *hampi* ceremony at the beginning of the rainy season, each peasant receiving a piece of sacred gourd which he then buries; the respecting of a certain number of tabous in the fields such as eating while walking, working on Sundays, lighting fires, etc.

Drought and locusts cause shortages, if not famines, such as those of 1900-1903, 1913-1914, 1926-1927, 1929-1931, 1944, 1945-1955, 1969-1973. The traditional response is twofold: the village population disperses into the bush, picking fruit and seeds to survive; grain is bought, at one time by selling children as slaves and for the last few decades by selling livestock which has prospered during the better years.

For a long time the strategy of land use of the Zarma peasant has had to provide for both his physical security and his food requirements. Up till the beginning of the century, raids by the Tamachek nomads constituted the main danger, making it necessary to group the population on two different levels: regionally by making a densely-populated zone where the villages were close enough to support each other; on the village level by concentrating homes on good defense sites (steep valley slopes, valley floors with trees). The concentration of people (villages of an average of 200 inhabitants) gave rise to a concentric ring pattern of cultivated land. The first village belt, the *hali*, is made up of enclosed gardens heavily manured with domestic waste. Here, the more delicate crops are grown: various *Hibiscus* (some of which for cloth fibre, and okra for its fruit); sesame for its oil-bearing seeds; gourds, the sale of which helps to pay the taxes. Beyond the gardens, the *koïratié* is a more or less circular stretch of land completely cleared of vegetation. Here the fields are cultivated for 6 to 7 years in alternance with short fallow periods of 2 to 3 years. A patch of useful trees is conserved: *Acacia albida* which adds to soil fertility; *A. nilotica* and *Balanites aegyptiaca* both provide leaves and fruits for cattle fodder; *Sclerocarya birrea* with very hard wood is used for making tool handles, etc. The various varieties of millet are cultivated in the *koïratié*; the land is lightly fertilized by ashes and domestic waste or by the village livestock which remain there during the dry period. Beyond these are the *zighi*, blocks of fields isolated in the bush which were often unsafe during the time of raids. More recently the distance from the village and the necessity of watching over the crops against predation means that the peasants send a member of their family to stay there during the growing season. Crops are still grown by shifting cultivation; the millet crop, most often associated with cow-pea (*Vigna sinensis*) and red sorrel grown at the field edges, last for several years, then the *zighi* is moved on.

This spatial strategy, strongly influenced by the age-old need for defense, has been replaced in the last thirty or forty years on the regional and village levels by spreading settlements over vast new territories. This expansion is also a response to the rapid increase in population. In the Zarmaganda-Anzourou area the population has in fact tripled in about thirty years: 41,500 people recorded in 1934; in 1944, 66,600; in 1955, 91,700; in 1965, 122,900. Pioneers pushed the Zarmaganda frontiers northwards into the lands traditionally occupied by nomads giving as a result a more Sahel-type people: 51 per cent of the population lives between isohyets 450 and 500 mm, and 36 per cent in regions with less than 450 mm rainfall. Villages have multiplied. From 1940 to 1965 the number of officially recognized villages has gone from 100 to 236. Around these villages many hamlets, or *kwariyey*, are found. For example, the village of Kossi-Tondi, situated 35 km North of Oualam (14°53'), possesses some 2,500 ha of land on which the vegetation was first cleared in 1880. In 1972, three new hamlets were spread out over this area: Barké-Koira created in 1930; Baki-Koira created in 1951 and Zibo-Koira created in 1957. The reasons behind such growth need to be emphasized. The numbers of heavy livestock tripled between 1940 and 1970. Official records show that at present, there are 45,000 heads of cattle in the region, which means that numbers are more likely to be around 100,000 to 150,000, giving about 1 head of cattle per person which is high for a peasant population. It is not easy to organize homesteads and fields into large units and also increase herd size. This means that everything is spread out, which can be disadvantageous to the peasant in that there is a loss of manuring, and that the herds need to be watched either by village herdsmen or else by the Foulani, resulting in a loss of income (milk, loss of animals through negligence or dishonesty) for the owner. On the other hand, the traditional rules controlling land ownership contribute to this territorial extension. At Kassi-Tondi the founders of the *kwariyey* are the sons of the women, i.e. the village women who have married outsiders. The customary land-tenure law excludes them from collective land ownership which is strictly reserved for the men's descendants. Cultivation being less competitive further away from the village, it is a logical decision for the marginal individuals of the village society to settle at the periphery of the village limits when there no longer is any danger and also where economic conditions and the growing numbers of livestock oblige them to do so. In 1972, for a population of 235 at Kassi-Tondi, the three hamlets totaled 72 inhabitants.

The spatial strategy of loosening the village bonds and extending territorial limits is accompanied by significant changes in the methods of cropping. On the one hand, under a parkland of 'useful' trees, the fertility of the village fields is maintained by domestic waste and especially plant residue (the millet straw is put on the soil after the harvest). On the other hand, the *kwariyey* fields benefit from regular fertilization by the owners' cattle which are corralled there during the dry season, moving each month so as to evenly manure all the fields. Manure is also provided by the animals belonging to the Foulani who install their straw huts around the *kwariyey*. The neighbouring bush is thus heavily fertilized and the grazed fallow - manured field combination is much more systematic. In the village cropping system, a fairly wide diversity of traditionally cultivated plants and varieties is used. In the *kwariyey* agricultural system, millet is dominant.

Although the Zarma peasant is skilled in making the best of new regional conditions, he has not been able to incorporate significant changes in his agricultural system. Ground-nut cultivation has not been developed, as rainfall is too scarce. An introduced quick-growing millet, *ankousteir*, has not been adopted as the ears are too short for making bundles car-

ried on the head. The *Allen* cotton, cultivated up till 1950-1955 and whose sale made it possible to increase the numbers of cattle, has been dropped because of the introduction of imported cotton goods. Nevertheless, the Zarma peasant is marked by the trading civilization of this zone, and is strongly attracted by every sort of transaction. In addition to the sale of gourds (a good crop, requiring very little work and whose fruits sell easily), the Kassi-Tondi Zarma people speculate in the various markets they frequent. In Balayera they buy natron, fanpalm leaves and straw mats which they then resell at the Mangaizé market. The Zarma strategy essentially consists of a kind of manoeuvre in space adapted to the conditions of the moment, but the land-tenure regulations provide the stimuli, induce marginal individuals to move away, and impose the limits, that is, the very existence of a village territory, these boundaries following the traces of the axe of the first men who cleared the forest and whose sons form the community perpetuated by a father-to-son lineage.

THE DOGON PEASANTS

The spatial strategy of the Zarmas cannot be used by the Dogon peasants of the Bandiagara Plateau (Mali). Many studies have been made of these people from an ethnological point of view particularly concerning their spatial movements (Gallais 1965, 1975).

Some 300,000 Dogons occupy two very different natural environments in the loop of land made by the River Niger between latitudes 13° 30' and 15° North. The Bandiagara Plateau is made of blocks of hard sandstone split open by narrow sandy ravines. The Séno is an immense pediment plain dominated by the vertical edge of the Plateau. The Falaise (cliff) rises up 200 to 300 m and its vast sandy areas stretch to the East. The 150,000 Dogons of the Plateau and the Falaise suffer from the harsh climate: rainfall varies between 650 and 500 mm. Droughts are formidable, causing scarcities and famines; those of 1913-1914 had effects on the population which were not attenuated until about 1935. Several advantages must be noted, however: the sandstones maintain numerous springs and rainfall seems a little more abundant on the Plateau than on the plains around it.

The occupation of this Plateau is the result of historical events. The ancient Dogon country, set up against the Falaise, where cave-dwellings are evidence of ancient occupation, essentially covered the vast plains of the Séno. This occupation was reduced due to pressure by the Mossi, the Foulani and the Tamachek peoples, and in the

19th century most of the Dogons had taken refuge in the admirably designed defensive villages in the Falaise or on the Plateau. Since the colonial era, this ancient Dogon country has slowly been becoming depopulated due to extensive immigration to the new Dogon country of Séno, but the traditional ecosystem still persists on the Plateau.

This ecosystem owes its existence to a certain political strategy. When the Séno plain occupied by the Dogon villagers became extremely unsafe, three options were possible. Firstly, surrender to the Mossi and Foulani invaders, pay tributes and become captives, as was the case of a certain number of Rimaïbé villages of the plain, captured by the Foulani. Secondly, resist in the plain by occupying the land in tightly-spaced groups of sizeable villages, accepting the continuously unpredictable climate; such was the choice of the Houmbébé people of Mondoro, who lived more or less at liberty in the plain, but who, during the 19th century, moved their settlements three times over 100 km, had people and livestock massacred, and ended up asking the protection of the Hombou Songhai, enemies of the Foulani, but almost as demanding. Thirdly, take refuge in the Falaise and on the Plateau; such was the decision of the majority of Dogons of the plain and the origin of the villages situated on citadels, or scree slopes or hidden in ravines, which still can be admired today. This last choice was particularly difficult as it involved squeezing a large population onto tiny areas of very poor arable land, since this was reduced to a few ravines or sandy gullies embedded in the sandstone. This was possible only within the context of a very strict institutional system collectively governing the interactions between man and the land.

Each unit of collective housing, the *bô*, i.e. the village or the quarter in administrative terminology, used to group the members of the *gina*, a father-to-son community with an average of 200 to 300 persons. The *gina* collectively owns the houses and the *lara*, i.e. the permanently cultivated land, often representing the entire arable area. The chief of the *gina*, the oldest man of the oldest lineage, is essentially responsible for carrying out the farming rites, especially those which take place in the foundation house of the village (*ginagara*) in which he lives. Each *gina* chief that comes to office presides over a group assembly which distributes houses and land according to the age in order of each family chief, the oldest receiving the *lara* fields the closest to the *bô*, and according to the needs and the labour force of each family. All the fields of the *lara* are *miné dié*, i.e. fertilized plots, cultivated collectively by the men and women of the same family. The *bala*, beyond the *lara*, is a part of the land which is not systematically distributed amongst the community; it is collectively owned and anyone can clear and cultivate as much as he wishes. The *bala* is particularly the domain of the *minédiom* cultivated individually by adolescents, women and brothers of family chiefs for their own personal needs, each having a free day in five (the animistic week lasting five days), one day in seven for Moslems. Collective land appropriation, periodic redistribution of the most useful land and gerontocratic ruling give the settlement an egalitarian cohesion as well as a religious meaning to the bonds uniting the land and the collectivity as a whole. In such a system, the forms of economic domination are avoided thanks to the periodical redistribution of the means of production. For the individual, all this attenuates the harshness of the environmental conditions.

The second major element of the Dogon withdrawal strategy was the creation of an institutional framework to defend and rule the settlement. Several *bô* make up a distinct geographical territory within a very small area, since the *bô* are generally a few hundred meters from each other, at most one or two kilometers.

- This geographical territory has first of all a clan unity showing a common mythical origin appearing in the family name and the sharing of a patrimony symbolizing the age-old possession of the plain. In the present migrations, this creates a strong bond between the pioneers of the same clan.
- Religiously and legally, the collectivity is institutionalized in the personage of the *hogon* and his officers.
  From within his dwelling, the *hogon* carries out the ritual sacrifices before seeding time; he judges all matters of theft, rape and murder. His sacred and inspired character can only be preserved by his isolation: a virgin brings him food, he wears particularly distinguishing clothes and adornments, he only communicates with the people through his officers, the *serou*, numbering five or six.
- There is also a group arrangement for war. War chiefs, selected for their courage and their skill, train the generations making up the territorial defenders.
- Finally, this territory possesses an economic life of its own, due to a series of

markets. These small markets are organized on a five-day week basis, they take place in four or five *bô* and the day of the week is designated by the name of the place where it is held. The existence of these markets ensures an active social life (marriages, information), enables the exchange of produce and confers a real solidarity within a very limited area. In all his relations with the outside world, the Dogon peasant places himself in this territorial and social setting.

The Dogon people must confront the particular difficulties of farming in an extremely confined area. As a result, various techniques are used to manage hillslopes for intensive cropping. Hillslopes are converted into terraces; ridges 50 cm high are constructed on the cultivated sands to catch the rain; a parkland of 'useful' trees, far denser than would occur naturally, is set aside as is the time-honoured custom; a considerable amount of manure is obtained from the smaller livestock kept with continually renewed bedding in the inner courtyards of the houses; the land is improved by adding more fertile soil. The Dogon peasant has particularly ingenious techniques for conserving and improving his environment, which do, however, involve considerable work. He thus obtains yields that are higher than those of extensive agriculture in the plains. He disposes of a great many varieties of millet; for example at Kassa there are five varieties of sorghum. He practises rain-fed rice cultivation which is exceptional at this latitude. He conserves the traditional cultivation of elusine millet and he sows beans and red sorrel at the field edges.

However the Dogon people are particularly skilled in irrigated agriculture and in conserving their harvests. Great quantities of harvested produce are stored, either in isolated granaries or in the upper stories of their huts. The Dogons are particularly vulnerable to the scarcities caused by drought and have a religious tradition relating to these phenomena which they consider follow a seven-year cycle. They relate their major festivities to this seven-year rotation and their storage policy is adapted to this cycle, trying to conserve several years' harvests in the granaries. Reserves of grain, fruit, berries and cotton remain in excellent condition thanks to the granary construction and maintenance techniques, insect and rodent control and protection against humidity using a coating of a powdery mixture of saltpeter, ashes and various crushed woods.

Irrigated agriculture is very characteristic of the Dogon gardens. One of the first para-doxes is that this type of agriculture is practised in an area of scanty water supply (the springs have a limited flow) whereas it is not found in the Niger valley. A second paradox lies in the absence of any water-raising device: the Dogon people ignore even the most rudimentary shaduf, or Persian wheels. As they are unable to bring water to their fields, they are often obliged to do the reverse, i.e. construct a garden on the rocky ground next to the water hole by bringing a considerable amount of arable earth in small baskets carried on the head. There again, watering is done by gourd, taking considerable time and great efforts in manually fetching and drawing water. In a few favoured sites, the hillslope gardens are placed downslope of the springs which means that they are watered via gravity. The inhabitants of these arid plateaux can sell vegetables (tomatoes, onions, sweet potatoes, pimentos), fruit and tobacco to the valley population, which is really astonishing.

These high yielding cash-crop productions could lead to exclusive specialization. The careful Dogon peasant thinks otherwise and continues a less profitable millet agriculture. The Dogon strategy tends to conserve the basis of food self sufficiency. This basis, which is amply provided for in the good years, allows him to sell millet at the Niger Valley markets, even in times of scarcity when prices rise. This is an amazing achievement for peasants who dispose of 2 to 3 ha of mediocre land per family of 7 to 10 persons.

On the whole, the strategy of the Dogon people who took refuge on the Plateau was successful in sustaining high population densities in a very unpropitious environment, making self-defense possible. Through this strategy, a social and spatial organization evolved, which, although rather undeveloped and weak on the political level (which largely explains their inferiority with respect to the Mossi and the Foulani), was nevertheless sufficient to establish close-knit communities. Through considerable work in maintaining the land, they also succeeded in meeting the food requirements and obtaining higher yields than their neighbours without using fallow rotation.

THE RICE-GROWERS OF THE NIGER INTERIOR DELTA

Since the river valleys of the Sudan-Sahel zone are so important, an analysis should be made of the traditional strategies of the populations living on the marshy alluvial washes forming the interior deltas not only of the Niger, but also around Lake Chad and on the White Nile.

Why have the wide river valleys of this area not given rise to intense human settlement and to the powerful hydraulic techniques that they seem to need? It is surprising to find that this potential has not been exploited, particularly as it would be especially valuable at these latitudes. It is thus astonishing to discover the existence of well-established peasant-farming populations such as the *Marka* or *Rimaïbé* rice growers of the Niger interior delta (Gallais 1967). The soils of the flood plains are poor, slightly acid, with very low calcium content; they are fertile only in the lowest basins, but these low-lying areas of the plain are submerged for six to eight months of the year and are uncovered only from March to July (a period of extreme drought when no cropping is possible). In addition, even if the sandy or sandy-loam soils found in the upper part of the flood plain can be worked by the rice-growers, the clay soils or the low-lying basins are compact; when they are moist they stick to the spade; when dry, they crack, harden, and can only be worked with an exhausting amount of effort. The irregularity of the climate is, moreover, reflected by the extreme irregularity of waterflow. The Niger floodwaters reach very different levels according to the years (the maximum recorded at Mopti shows a difference of more than one and a half meters, the arrival of a certain level of floodwater can be delayed or advanced by several weeks). The rice cultivation of the Niger interior delta is subject to climatic and hydraulic risks by firstly depending on the rains and secondly on the arrival of sufficient but not excessive riverwater.

Historical constraints largely explain man's relatively weak hold over the Niger interior delta, particularly concerning agriculture. Various evidence testifies to the existence of a much denser human occupation and a richer agriculture at the end of the great Sudan Empires, the Mali Empire (13th to 15th century) and the Songhai Empire (16th century). From the 17th century onwards, the plains bordering the Niger attracted waves of invaders, some peasants like the Bambaras from Ségou whose armed throngs seemed to have disrupted rather than enriched the country, some others stockmen like the Foulani who dominated the country from the 17th to the 19th century. This domination had without a doubt a disorganizing effect from the point of view of the regional peasant civilizations: ceaseless wars, displacements of population, remodelling of territorial structures to facilitate the movement of livestock, social subdual of the peasants and disappearance of their own livestock[1]. The

aristocratic and Islamic Foulani domination confined the various races of the region in areas whose ecosystems had become highly specialized by the interplay of technical traditions and a land tenure system that made a distinction between owning water and owning grass or land. Recent events have reduced these differences which nevertheless remain a fundamental cultural characteristic. This explains why in these vast open plains, various peoples lived alongside each other, each using one of the possibilities of the environment, but neither being able to completely develop the country.

All these conditions taken together strongly influence the strategy of the Marka rice growers, traditional peasants of the flood plains, and also of the *Rimaïbé* rice growers, agricultural captives of the Foulani. Considerable differences divide the two groups and reflect their own particular situations throughout history.

The rice growers' strategy is to dispose of various types of land within the village territory. This explains the higher population densities on the banks of the flood plains which offer a mixture of types - rain-fed millet agriculture and paddyfield rice cultivation. The villages situated in the middle of the flood plains usually have an area of higher land which is used for rain-fed crops harvested in October. These are fossil dunes or a river embankment that is either not reached at all by the floodwaters or else later on in the season. These latter form flooded uplands which can be used for planting stiff-stemmed rice requiring very little submersion and also for flood retreat crops (manioc, sweet potatoes, groundnuts, sorghum) which are started in November fairly soon after the flood retreat so that the harvest can be gathered before the desiccating March winds. Rice is cultivated generally in August when the rice has grown sufficiently after the rains. It is especially grown on the *feya*, embankments of average height submerged by two meters of water at the peak of flooding during an average year, and in deeper hollows (*pondo*) covered by three to five meters of water which can be used for cultivating certain varieties of rice (the pond that remains at low water is used for collective fishing). These different levels of agricultural land allow a maximum crop diversity. This diversification is also obtained by systematically

1. The *Dina*: from 1818 to 1862 the Foulani Empire of Cheikou Ahmadou made an enthusiastic attempt at regional reorganization in order to reconcile agriculture and pastoralism, but this did not last long and was interrupted by the Toucouleur invasion.

using a great many varieties. The *Oryza gla-berrima* varieties are very close to their wild counterparts; their numbers and their plastic-ity show that their characteristics are not definitely fixed. Each region of the Delta, sometimes each village, has a set of varieties adapted to its own soil conditions. Each peas-ant has several plots of land: one upland plot devoted to early rice varieties providing food in times of scarcity; one or several larger plots sown with semi-late or late varieties. This staggering of varieties is used first of all for safety. Unable to predict the flood-water level or the amount of rainfall, the peasant does not use selected varieties re-quiring specific growing conditions. Rather, he prefers the safety offered by a whole range of regional varieties adapted as much to a quick rise in waterlevel as to an unchanging waterlevel, or there again to insufficient water. This same concern explains the mixture of varieties sown in each plot: such and such a variety resists being attacked by rice-eating fish, another is more early-growing. This spacing out of ear formation with the losses that it implies at the time of harvesting is preferable to the risk of having the whole crop destroyed.

Another adaptation of the rice-grower to en-vironmental conditions is to constantly change the location of his fields. This is usually done by collective rotation of all the village fields. Popular tradition believes that the maxima and minima floodwater levels follow a 4 to 7-year cycle. The data available over thirty years clearly shows that even counting exceptional years there is in fact a certain cycle. For example, from 1951 to 1959, the flood levels were relatively high, except for 1956 which was low. As a result, when it ap-pears that a new cycle of high or low flood levels is beginning, the rice-growers move the paddyfields up on to higher ground or vice-versa.

The study of the village of Sévéri under-taken successively in 1949, 1958 and 1968 shows that this type of agriculture 'shifts' over a vast territory. In 1950, the population to-taled 470 inhabitants; in 1956, 548; in 1971, 730. Once captives of the Ouro-Daïebé Foulani, by traditional law these Rimaïbé peasants have no definite agricultural territory of their own. However, the land-tenure system has changed and they now freely dispose of some 1,300 ha of territory, of which 1,150 ha are flood plains at different elevations. The population density of the village territory (50 inhabitants/km^2) is much higher than the regional average (in 1970 about 20 inhabitants/

km^2). In spite of this crowding, Sévéri does not have a stable, structured land-use pattern but rather a series of temporary, successive cultivated fields at different levels of the flood plain. The major steps in the practice of this shifting rice cultivation have been:
- about 1940, cultivation in the Naval plain of average elevation;
- from 1943 to 1951, exploitation of the low-lying plains of Workouma-Koubaye during a cycle of low flood levels;
- from 1952 to 1956, cultivation of the al-luvial embankments due to the high flood levels;
- after the low flood level of 1956, another shift towards the plains of average eleva-tion, Naval, Feya Benté.

These movements were accompanied by the choice of different crop varieties, although, on the whole, rice cultivation at Sévéri has been dom-inated by late growing types: in 1948, the *djenneo balédio* variety, adapted to the slow drying out of the low-lying basins; in 1957-1958, 10 varieties of rice were recorded, occupying 5 to 54 per cent of the surface area. This mixture of varieties has also been found in individual plots.

The lay-out of the fields and the surface area cultivated have also been modified accord-ing to the flood water level. In 1949, 448 ha were cultivated in 115 plots for 139 workers, i.e. 3.22 ha/worker, and the average surface area per plot was 3.9 ha. In 1958, the total area was reduced to 359 ha for 157 workers, i.e 2.28 ha/worker and 1.24 ha/plot. As the alluvia embankments which provide the highest rice fiel are more undulating than the low-lying plains, the cultivated plots must be made smaller, and each farm must possess several plots. The Sévéri villagers were unable to continue culti-vating the same total surface area, as the up-land areas suitable for rice cultivation were limited. The second reason for the considerable reduction in the area cultivated per worker was that the 1957 harvest was very poor, because, with the 1956 flood level lower than in previou years, the rice fields were not located in the best areas. Many families lacked rice for seed-ing and the surface area sown was reduced. In 1968-1969, due to low flood levels, the relativ ly low-lying plains were once again sown with traditional rice varieties, thus coming back to the sites around Workouma which were culti-vated in about 1950. The spread of the use of stiff-stemmed rice varieties has, however, lead to an increase in upland rice cultivation on the farthest river embankments; the seeded area covered nearly 645 ha, i.e. 0.88 ha/person as compared to 1.18 ha in 1949 and 0.82 ha in 1956.

The Séveri example clearly shows the strategy used by the delta rice-growers and its limitations; it consists of a very hazardous game of shifting the rice fields over very small areas and of choosing rice varieties which in an average year produce very little extra to be sold. With average yields of 600 to 800 kg of paddy/ha, each villager has a surface area of 0.8 to 1.2 ha from which he obtains 500-800 kg; he himself requires an average of 3.68 kg/week of rice for food, i.e. nearly 200 kg/year (Missoes 1961).

This traditional strategy can be improved upon technically if the techniques used are efficient as well as appropriate, and if they do not create unfavourable side-effects in other sectors. The introduction of higher yielding Asiatic rice at the beginning of the century shows that this is possible, although the very precise submersion requirements are incompatible with the irregularity of the Niger flood water levels, so much so that the peasant continues to sow most of the land with traditional rice varieties. The broad-minded outlook of the rice-growers is also shown by the increase in the numbers of ploughs, which doubled from 1955 to 1970 (5,000 to 10,000 in the Mopti and Ké Macina Districts). This change lead to a very great increase in the surface area sown, but its effect was limited by the fact that weeding must be done at a specific time. Weeding is time-consuming as the paddyfields are invaded by wild rice, one of the consequences of shifting the plots. The main advantages of the plough were the gain in time and effort, and the restoration of a considerable amount of stock-raising based on work animals. On the other hand, the industrial handling of paddy for which paddyfields were set up at Diafarabé and Nantaka, has had no response and the factories are practically idle. The peasant and his wife prefer to husk paddy by pestle for their food, rather than sell paddy to then buy rice. The amount of surplus rice to be sold is insufficient for the proper collection of paddy to be organized well. Finally, the rice delivered to the factory consists of a mixture of varieties which give a poorly· bleached product with 15 to 20 per cent fragments, unsuitable for exportation. With respect to agricultural water-engineering projects, the peasants show a lucid and critical interest.

As a whole, the strategy of the delta rice-growers is based on a highly-developed adaptation to environmental variations. Very little interest is shown in varieties with specific requirements, even if they produce higher yields; the extension of fields with the plough is practised only when other agricultural work is completed, work which is lengthy and hand executed because the fields are dispersed and constantly moved, two other adaptations to the irregularity of the flood waters.

THE OUOLOF PEOPLE OF THE LOWER SENEGAL VALLEY

In the lower Senegal valley downstream of Dagana lies the village of Guidakar situated a few hundred meters from the water's edge. It stands isolated in the flood plains, the *oualo*, and a track 6 km long links it with the tarmacked road which follows the dry river terraces (*diéri*) from Richard Toll to Dagana. The village population is entirely Ouolof, but made up of a mixture of clans. The N'gueye are the founders, but by tradition the chiefs come from the Ndiaori clan. The major Ouolof clans, Seye, Taye, Nian, Ndiaye, Ouad, Diop and Seck are each represented by several families. Each family owns lands that are very unequally distributed. The multiplicity of clans and the family appropriation of land explains perhaps why the village has not been able to carry out any major collective developments. A river embankment protecting the *oualo* was constructed by an earth-moving machine hired from the administration; this embankment is maintained each year by the young people of the village. A co-operative farm was founded in 1962 but does not seem very active. A school taking in 33 boys, no girls, was constructed at the initiative and with the support of the United States Peace Corps. A welfare centre is to be built by the administration. Traditional strategy is therefore characterized by the lack of collective development.

There seems to be more efficient demographic control with respect to maintaining a stable population in an already densely-populated territory. At the beginning of the century, as soon as the Mauritanian side of the river became free of nomadic raids, families settled on the opposite bank and founded Guidakar-Mauritania and Kharri. The population greatly increased from the 1950s onwards; population records indicate 425 inhabitants in 1958, 573 inhabitants in 1964. However, seasonal and permanent emigration was high and, in 1972, only 500 inhabitants were recorded. Thus the population pressure was hardly alleviated. The 500 ha of traditional territory was cut back when about 150 ha were set aside as classified forest, raising the population density to 140 inhabitants/km². However, much of the *oualo* and *diéri* land remains uncultivated. No doubt the land-tenure system contains restrictions which explain this contradiction. This has been analyzed in several villages of the valley, for example at Kanel near Matan where 'the land-tenure system chases man out of the *oualo*. Paradoxically, the soil is underexploited and land is lacking' (Ravault 1964). The under-exploitation of the *oualo* is linked to the development of rice cultivation. The dominant trend is to make rice cultivation the centre of the economy and to substitute a cash-crop economy for a diversified and largely self-sufficient economy. The peasants cultivate millet in the *diéri* in order to buy rice for food; rice also signifies public aid, and organized and easy commercialization. The extension of rice cultivation is, however, limited by the relatively poor development of the Guidakar *oualo*. This is why the peasants want to benefit from a project of the SAED, the Société d'Aménagement et d'Exploitation du Delta (Delta Management and Exploitation Company), which, in addition to organizing the colonization of the Delta itself, manages the development of the low-lying basins along the river.

The Senegal River was traditionally a link with the lands on the Mauritanian bank where families from the communities had settled and which was considered as part of the village territory. This extra land is no longer available, and it is thus no longer possible to freely bring in produce from that area. A few years ago, the higher prices paid on the Northern bank incited the peasants to sell their surplus rice there. The recent monetary reform in Mauritania, which does not belong to the franc zone, inhibits profit-making from local production.

The village strategy was therefore deprived of the Mauritanian bank, of a part of the territory transformed into classified forest, and even of the river itself, traditionally considered as a highway for trade, allowing speculation on the goods for sale. Pushed back into the part of the *oualo* used for rice cultivation, this strategy tends to introduce land management techniques modelled on nearby development projects. Rather than taking the decision to carry out such developments, the village community is apparently waiting in the hope that something will be done, an attitude which may dissimulate taking active steps to induce the State to make such interventions.

IMPORTANT CHARACTERISTICS OF THE TRADITIONAL STRATEGIES OF THE SUDAN-SAHEL ZONE

Zarmaganda illustrates the situation in the most extensive areas of this zone: plateaux of sand or hard pan with a relatively low population density, conflicts with the nomadic peoples, isolation from urban trading centres.

The Dogon Plateau illustrates the group strategy of populations that had to 'dig in' to save themselves. The rice-growers of the Niger interior delta and the Ouolof people of the Senegal valley illustrate two different aspects of the relations between the inhabitants of the vast flood plains and their environment. These vario strategies have certain characteristics in comm

The need for food security is the fundamental problem; this is emphasized by the figures for protein and calorie rations calculated for each country and for regional studies:

	Daily rations	
	calories (kcal)	protein (g)
Chad	2,240	78
Mali	2,130	68
Mauritania	1,990	73
Niger	2,170	78
Senegal	2,300	64
Upper Volta	2,060	70

The minimal requirements are considered to be 2,100 kcal and 58 g of protein.

Demographic and economic investigation in a nomadic area of Niger (1966):

	Kilocalories		Protein (g)	
	actual	required	actual	required
farmers	1,913	1,997	73	55
stockmen	1,885	2,039	73	55

Socio-economic study of the Senegal Central Valley (1962):

	2,214	2,097	93	40

Whilst the protein requirements seem to be sufficiently covered thanks to stock-raising, the calorie ration is often barely made available. Calorie requirements are not met in dry years, a situation which justifies serious concern about food security.

Food security is essentially sought through rain-fed crops. These are the basic crops as muc in the Dogon area where there are irrigated cash-crops, as in the flood plains where hydro-agricultural specialization seems to be the vocation. In the Senegal Valley, the millet crops of the *diéri* outnumber those of the *oualo*; in the Niger interior delta, millet predominates in the various cultivated areas and, in the flooded plains, the smallest of sites are used for its cultivation. As the Sudan-Sahel farmers are not familiar with water-engineering techniques, they are resigned to adapting to the extremely irregular rainfall. However, rain-fed cultivation limits farming activities to a two and a half month period, during which the peasant is very busy. The yearly requirements must be covered by 75 days of work. This obligation explains why the peasant gives priority to the productivity of his work rather than to the yield per unit area. Everything which increases the total weight of grain is considered favourably; everything which might decrease it is rejected by an empirical yet accurate calculation. When land is unlimited and open, the peasant tries to increase his productivity by various strategies of distributing his crops; when land is limited, as on the Dogon Plateau, the peasant is obliged to ensure his food supply by increasing yields at the cost of lowering work productivity. The Dogon peasants who are currently colonizing the Séno are nevertheless coming back to their habitual strategy.

To deal with the hazardous climate, the peasant systematically uses a mixture of cultivated varieties, sticks to those which have proven themselves robust and adaptable, and staggers sowing times. All these methods do not serve to increase yields, but the peasant prefers to be sure of obtaining at least a minimum crop. The peasant also ensures his food supply by storing some of the harvest of good years. Everywhere the observer is struck by the number of granaries and the care taken in their maintenance. Building up the herds of livestock is a means by which the peasant can save up during peaceful years; the village granary can be defended in times of danger, but the mobile livestock can easily be stolen. The peasant thus comes back to a paeleonegritic tradition which has been conserved by a certain number of peoples. The Sérèr and the Dogon peoples have always kept large herds of various kinds of livestock because they conserved their ancient civilization and were independent with respect to the stockmen, whose influence led to the gradual wiping out of peasant livestock raising. Although livestock is usually considered as a food reserve, the animals are frequently used for working in the fields by the Dogon peasants, and moderately so by the Zarma. It is, moreover, remarkable to note that the best association of agriculture and pastoralism is practised by the most ancient negro populations.

Every new innovation or decision taken must thus give priority to the peasants' primordial concern for food security. A second social element of this peasant strategy must also be considered. The Sudan-Sahel peasant farmer has been influenced by centuries of village civilization. This tradition allows for both the concern for personal safety and the socio-religious aspects of peasant-land relationships. In Zarmaganda as well as in the Dogon country, personal safety implies a close network of villages of several hundred inhabitants making up the fairly dense territorial nuclei. The religious nature of the man-land relationships give the clans, or the descendants of the first men to clear the vegetation, the exclusive right to command the forces of nature. On these principles are based the peasant organization and settlement patterns. Cultivation can only be carried out if the peasants keep to the community that descends from those who cleared the land and whose chief is master of the land. This principle means that the village includes the group of families related to the chief and the families that settled afterwards; the land-tenure system usually recognizes this distinction. In general, the masters of the land, i.e. the village chiefs, accord the rights for long-term land exploitation fairly liberally, at least as long as the population level is not too high, but they are against breaking up the village or dispersing the family homes. Although the authority of the village chief can be refused and the spread of Islam has reduced the number of rites, the villages are nevertheless still strongly tied to tradition because of these socio-religious aspects.

Any strategies for the Sudan-Sahel zone must solve the problems posed by the village-based ideology. The dense network of villages means that the extensive cultivated areas of each village territory are contiguous or lie very close to each other. The peasant must travel several hundred meters, sometimes several kilometers, from his hut to his fields, posing transport problems for a peasant civilization that ignores the wheel and hardly ever uses cattle as beasts of burden. Settlement in a fixed location leads to the same phenomenon for cultivated areas. Soils are poor, however, and the methods of fertilization, although often efficient and ingenious, are usually insufficient. These difficulties are resolved to a greater of lesser degree by a variety of land-use patterns: the concentric rings of land of Zarmaganda; the rotation of land as described in the Sérèr country (Pélissier 1966); in the case of the Bouzou villages in Niger, the cultivated plot moves laterally each year (Nicolas 1962). In all these examples, there is a tendency to reduce the distance between the village and the fields to a minimum and to facilitate village stock-raising.

The traditional strategy tries to conciliate the concern for food security and the village-based ideology. The relationships between these two elements are obvious: food security is impossible without the village ensuring political security; the former also depends on the observing of rites which can only be carried out by the religious chief of the village community. On the other hand, the village exists within only a relative context of food security. When famines occur, the village splits up, and one finds that new villages are created in the regions of pioneer settlement. However, one wonders whether this interdependence of the two elements of the traditional strategy has resisted the changes that have marked the last 25 or 50 years. Indeed, in many regions where the population increase had doubled or tripled the population density in 30 or 50 years, the search for food security involves a spatial strategy on a huge scale: relative population dispersion between the villages and the cities and even colonisation on the peripheries. It is only these new lands that can give both an increase in productivity and an increase in yields. However, the village civilization is heading towards a crisis for the following reasons. Political security is ensured everywhere, the fundamental bonds and the religious authority of the masters of the land have become weaker, and the people are encouraged to produce more in order to sell their goods (not only millet but also ground-nuts and cotton). All the same, a man does not suddenly break away from such a powerful type of social existence as the traditional village society of the Sudan-Sahel zone. Sudden returns, frequent backtracking from the pioneer zones, an awareness of the social and cultural traumatism resulting from the abandon of the village context, are in this respect significant phenomena. The traditional strategy consists essentially in conciliating the two major requirements: food security and village-based ideology.

III. MODERN DECISION-MAKING FOR DEVELOPMENT PROJECTS

Modern development in the Sudan-Sahel zone aims at relatively simple objectives which can be formulated with a limited amount of technical intervention. One of these projects is the '30,000 ha' Project in the Senegal Delta; the other is the Programme for the Development of Stock-Raising in the Mopti Region (Mali). The first project can be analysed on the basis of ten years of results; as for the second, which was to begin in 1975, it can be discussed only in terms of problematical considerations. In spite of this difference of perspective, it seemed useful to bring them together because they are complementary: the 30,000 ha Project is concerned with rice and is based on a policy of new settlements; the Mopti Project is concerned with pastoralism and includes the resident population.

THE SENEGAL DELTA 30,000 HA PROJECT

The Senegal Delta is the site of a vast operation for colonisation and mechanised rice cultivation called the 'Opération des 30 000 ha'. In 1974, 10,000 ha were being cultivated, 8,500 colonists had settled, and, taking the neighbouring traditional populations into account, nearly 25,000 people were involved. At present, this is the largest although not the only project in the Senegal Valley, which is to be the object of an overall development scheme.

Decision-making

The development of the Senegal Delta is the end result of a decision which can be broken into three steps, each one having its own ideology and choice of techniques.
- For more than a century, from 1815 to the beginning of the 20th century, the proximity to the Delta of the capital of Senegal, Saint-Louis, focused the colonist population's attention on this area, where it was planned to try out and then produce the tropical plants necessary for 19th century Europe. As early as 1916, Governor Schmaltz recommended sugar, indigo and cotton development in the Oualo country, the Delta and the Lower Valley. In 1820, an agronomist named Richard created an experimental garden, Richard-Toll. In addition to trying out a great many tropical plants which, with the exception of the ground-nut, were hardly ever used afterwards, Richard introduced the shaduf, as he was persuaded that this device would spread in the Senegal Valley as it had in the Nile. But in 1975, none of this had occurred, showing that the peasant farmer populations of the West African Sudan-Sahel Valleys were reluctant to adopt small-scale irrigation techniques. In addition, Richard distributed some 50 lots of 130 ha amongst European and African planters, which represented the first colonisation. However,

Richard's work was abandoned in 1831. From 1856 to 1865, Faidherbe unsuccessfully took up similar experiments. At the end of the last century and at the beginning of the 20th century, economic projects were mostly concerned with ground-nut cultivation along the Dakar-Saint-Louis line, while plans for developing the Senegal Valley fell into second place.

- After the first World War, interest was once again directed towards the major African river valleys. This was the period when the Gézireh in Sudan was developed, and the Office du Niger was created. Several river management projects for both irrigation and navigation were planned, and the associated studies increased knowledge about this environment. It is thus that, owing to a project that in 1904 recommended the construction of several dams on the central and lower parts of the valley, it was realised that, because of the shallowness of the river gradient, flooding of immense areas would occur which would endanger the dense human populations of the valley. The upper part of the river was therefore surveyed and, in 1928, the Gouina site was proposed for a dam whose reservoir would hold about 9 billion[1] m^3. As early as 1918, Henri set forth the idea of developing the Delta itself by mechanised agriculture. These different projects engendered studies undertaken under the general authority of the Mission d'Etudes du fleuve Sénégal (Senegal River Study) which in 1938 became the Mission d'Aménagement du Sénégal (Senegal Development Programme).

Knowledge about the natural and human environment gradually increased. Floodwater dates and characteristics were documented, particularly concerning the very high flood-levels which occurred every 10 to 20 years: 1866, 1871, 1906, 1922, 1927, 1937, 1950; readings showed that the floodwaters accelerated in the 20th century, increasingly reducing the length of the period suitable for navigation. The rise in salt level in the river at low water and an increase in soil salinity were noted, conditions already observed by Henri for Lake Guiers.

The restrictions imposed by the human environment also promoted other studies. Gaden (1935) and Vidal (1935) noted the feudal characteristics of the land-use system. The colonial administration, which in 1903 abolished a land tax called the *assaka* (a tithe paid to the master of the land by all the farmers), hesitated to take further steps: the Senegal Valley was not an empty region like that dealt with by the Office du Niger during the same period. In addition, maps tracing transhumance (Bonnet-Dupeyron 1951) showed how the stockmen used the *oualo* and how various interests over-lapped.

During this second stage (1920-1960) of development planning, the valley was viewed as a foodstore for West Africa and especially for Senegal, complementing the ground-nut producing areas which were short of cereals; for, before 1939, Senegal was importing 60,000 t of rice from Indochina. In 1948 at Richard-Toll, 4 areas of paddyfields were constructed, irrigated by the water from Lake Guiers and protected from a rise in salt level by one of the first dams; some more areas of paddyfields were set up in the lower valley using the same techniques (irrigation by motor pump). It can be said that in the 1950s, the technique adopted for rice cultivation was irrigation using pumped water. The geographical situation in the Delta and in the lower valley was also established: 'The uninhabited Oualo country provides a good field for experimentation with today's European techniques' (Papy 1951). Two questions were left unanswered: first, expansion in the central valley, the Fouta Toro, which would involve managing the river by a dam upriver at Gouina together with a dam downriver at Dagana; and second, the type of management to be used in these development projects — the Richard-Toll system, family colonisation or traditional village units grouped together in co-operatives.

- The third stage of the decision came in the 1960s when people became aware of the serious demographic and social problems of the central valley, such as the emigration of the Toucouleur to Dakar. This emigration was studied by sociologists (Diop 1960) and instigated detailed social and demographic analyses of the valley populations (Boutillier 1962). The problems of the Fouta country could be attenuated by organized migration towards the Oualo country.

The SAED, the Société d'Aménagement et d'Exploitation du Delta (Delta Management and Exploitation Company), created in 1965, is a public institution officially concerned with agriculture, industry and trade. It has the following tasks:

---

1. In this Technical Note, the term 'billion' is used to mean 1×10^9.

1. take measures to develop, settle and cultivate public lands under its responsibility;
2. condition and sell the harvested produce;
3. assist the peasants grouped in co-operatives by creating a suitable administrative framework.

In 1965, the SAED was assigned the following objective for the decade 1965-1975: cultivation of 30,000 ha, to produce 80,000 t of paddy, through the settlement of 8,000 families, i.e. about 40,000 people. Three essential considerations which seem to have inspired the development policy for Lower Senegal are made apparent by this reconstitution of the various stages in decision-making. These three considerations are related to the project begun in 1965:

- It was expected that this project would have favourable side-effects on the economy of the Saint-Louis region which was slowly declining in the last 50 years. The action of a politically powerful pressure group from Saint-Louis at the end of the colonial era and since independence has not been insignificant in this respect.
- Rice production was to reduce the increase in rice importation (179,000 t in 1965, i.e. 4,476 million CFA francs for imports totalling 40,198 million CFA francs). The imported rice was indispensable for feeding the urban population and the people of certain areas where there were shortages, such as the central valley.
- It was hoped to slow down the migration from the central valley, which had already involved more than 70,000 people, and to redirect a part of this migration towards the delta by offering the new colonists higher incomes reaching 45 to 50,000 CFA francs per person against 20,000 in the traditional regions.

The 30,000 ha project has therefore responded more to regional and national objectives than local ones; the project does not consider the relatively small population of the delta.

Results of the decade 1965-1974

During this decade, the projects and studies for the development of the entire Senegal Valley were undertaken within the framework of inter-State organizations. The last of these, the Organisation pour la Mise en Valeur du Sénégal (OMVS) (Senegal Development Organization), continued the project of building a dam upriver at Manantali on the River Bafing, in conjunction with several dams in the central valley on the River Falémé, at Saldé for irri-gating the Island at Morfil, and for irrigating Diama in the delta.

The project results for this decade can be summarized in four parts:

- the national and regional objectives;
- the well-being and social equilibrium of the colonist community;
- the traditional peoples of the region;
- the environment.

The project has not reached its own objectives

- In 1975, the surface area cultivated in the delta was 8,034 ha. Including the low-lying basins which have been developed outside the delta, the SAED was supporting 9,594 ha cultivated for rice, of which only 2,794 ha had complete water management (so called *tertiary* development).
- The colonist community had increased by 8,500 people.
- In 1969-1970, SAED rice production reached 11,000 t.

After certain disappointments following the main construction work and the annual recruitment campaigns, it was decided to pause from 1965 to 1967. The 1968 flood necessitated the installation of new pumping stations. Soil salinization was greater than predicted, and lead to leaching and drainage experiments whose prohibitive cost (1 million CFA francs per ha) meant that they were unlikely to be continued. It was realized that the available scientific information, although abundant, was insufficient.

The main national objective to reduce cereal importation was not reached. Indeed, imports have continued to rise for the last ten years:

253,229 t in 1966
320,750 t in 1969
426,553 t in 1973

i.e. the equivalent of 14,743 million CFA franc for a total of 80,166 million CFA francs of imports.

It is more difficult to evaluate the project's success with respect to its regional objectives. The population increase of the Saint-Louis urban agglomeration continues: 1960, 60,000 inhabitants; 1974, 100,000 inhabitants (town council estimate); but it is doubtful whether the SAED has contributed towards the town's activities. As for the migration of people from the central valley, the 30,000 ha project has had an insignificant effect, giving a drop of about 1,000 people. It was calculated that for 3 Toucouleurs from the valley, 1 was living in Dakar (Lericollais and Vernière 1975).

Welfare and social equilibrium of the colonist community

The colonists live in the five villages created since 1965 (M'Boundoum Est, M'Boundoum Nord, M'Boundoum-Barrage, Kassack Nord, Kassack Sud), in principle each comprising 200 huts. The geometric lay-out, the monotony of identical huts, the ugliness of certain structures such as the domed huts of M'Boundoum-Barrage, the absence of trees or hedges, and the vast dusty, empty open spaces which were considered worth conserving, collectively give an impression of morosity and emptiness in contrast to the lively social life of the traditional villages. Each family receives a 2.5 to 3 ha plot of land. The SAED maintains the water engineering and road network free of charge and, at great expense, provides the colonists with machines for ploughing and harvesting, selected seed and fertilizer. The colonists are grouped in co-operative farms and sell their surplus produce to the SAED, deducting a payment for the cultivation costs of approximately 5 qx/ha.

Through the co-operatives, the peasants are becoming increasingly indebted to the SAED and an already lengthy moratorium has to be extended each year. In 1969, the amount overdue came to 105 million CFA francs; in 1970, 108 million CFA francs. The SAED policy does not allow for initiative on the part of the subsidised peasants. For all technical matters, including these concerning the 50 ha unit of irrigated land, the peasant is in fact an agricultural worker, just as in a commercial enterprise. The cultivated area is depersonalized, since each year the fields are collectively rotated under primary or secondary management (partial water management).

From 1971, groups of farmers (10 to 15 family chiefs cultivating about 50 ha of land) were organized between the SAED civil servants and the colonists. The men began to develop a real feeling for the land once the cultivated area had been established through tertiary management, i.e. total control of water use (levelling, irrigation and drainage). This tertiary management, which in 1974 concerned 1,600 ha in the delta, makes it possible to double yields (3.5 t/ha predicted).

The colonists criticize the SAED for the high costs of the services provided and the low prices paid for paddies; for the inflexibility of regulations in general including errors in managing the accounts. For its part, the SAED complains of the amount of absenteeism and of indirect exploitation of certain civil servant-colonists or traditional peasants who have maintained their interests in their regions of origin. Although the colonists seem to have higher incomes than the traditional peasants, this does not help the social aspects of this project. The SAED does not appear to have succeeded in creating a responsible colonist community ready to adopt new techniques, nor a new, dynamic peasant society integrated with the region.

The populations of the regional environment

Apart from the new settlers, the development of the delta also more or less directly interests about thirty farming villages, of which certain families have received some plots within the paddyfield area. In addition, some villages have received SAED technical aid without, however, being integrated into its inflexible system. The village of Ronck (1,005 inhabitants in 1972), at the initiative of a remarkable leader, was able to organize its own completely independent co-operative farm. The villagers had become aware of their non-participation with the SAED developments and of the fact that they were getting deeper and deeper into debt. The peasants preferred to choose the seed and control flooding of the paddyfields themselves, calling upon SAED technical aid only when they considered it necessary. The village co-operative farm became a collective production unit, each co-operative farmer working 90 days per year on the collective area. This area has been gradually increasing in size (crops of tomatoes and rice):

Crop	1972-73	1973-74	1974-75	Planned extension
Tomatoes	6 ha	19 ha	43 ha	70 ha
Rice	23 ha	55 ha	185 ha	400 ha

The co-operative farm uses hand tools, but calls in SAED's help for ploughing the fields. In 1975-76, it hoped to buy its own tractor. A similar independence was demonstrated with the sale of produce. As the prices paid by the SOCAS canning-factory for the tomatoes of the delta were considered insufficient, the co-operative organized a parallel opening to sell tomatoes directly to Dakar. Another type of action consists in making ready for the return of the peasants who emigrated to Dakar and are trying to use the particular skills of the villagers themselves (mechanical skills, for example).

Each family chief in this co-operative receives a share of the profits, shares which have gradually increased with the extension of the areas under collective cultivation: in 1972-73, 8,000 CFA francs; in 1974-75, 100,000 CFA francs. These are net figures for one share, all costs being covered.

The Ronck balance-sheet appears to be very positive and exemplary. However, it is necessary to consider the particular conditions behind the success of this co-operative: an exceptional leader highly regarded as a member of the family that founded the village, with a broad, modern outlook developed when he was a school teacher; a geographical situation by which the co-operative could benefit from SAED support while remaining independent of its organization; a considerable amount of external aid from the State or international organizations, totaling 5 million CFA francs between 1970 and 1974.

A certain number of villages of the region therefore benefit from the development of the delta and from the services offered by the SAED. On the other hand, the stockmen who traditionally used the delta have had to move away or were obliged to change their activities (Hervouet 1971). Various groups of stockmen used the low-lying basins of the central delta as flood-retreat pastures. Amongst these, 1,500 Foulani owning approximately 8,000 heads of cattle have become rice-growers. These people are finding it increasingly difficult to both continue farming and keep their cattle, which are now sent away from the central delta from November to January up to the time of the rice harvest, at a time when they used to gather in this area. The stockmen-rice-growers have settled along the Saint-Louis-Ross Béthio road, between the *oualo* and the *diéri*. A co-operative dairy was founded to make a daily milk collection. These people have considerable difficulties, however, as land development *per se* outside the paddyfields has changed the deltaic environment. The Foulani are poorly integrated into the village co-operatives; the co-operative dairy had to come to a stop because of excessive costs (in 1969, an average 627 liters of milk were collected per day over a distance of 400 km). The Foulani that have permanently settled in the central delta and have opted for the monetary income from rice cultivation, are obliged to abandon their pastoral life and economy. Those who wish to continue some kind of stock-raising have to leave the delta, but it is difficult to find a substitute area. Further upriver, the densely-populated valley is already the scene of frequent conflicts between stockmen and peasant farmers. Further South, the banks of Lake Guiers are overgrazed. The Foulani therefore head towards the less densely-populated Mauritanian bank, with a loss of livestock and an important source of income for Senegal. One of the weaknesses of the SAED project in the central delta is that traditional stock-raising was not sufficiently taken into account. Generally speaking, the favourable or unfavourable consequences on the traditional regional populations have not been considered.

Environmental effects

The environment has certainly become more prone to wind erosion through clearing of vegetation, deep mechanized ploughing and increased wood felling. From January onwards, the delta becomes a bare dusty area scoured by the Northern trade winds. The disturbance of the natural drainage network and water pollution has seemingly modified the aquatic vegetation, which has harmful effects on the fish. Whilst the dam planned at the head of the delta will stop sea water intrusion in the river, irrigation may cause soil salinization. It is not certain that these problems were ever envisaged at the decision-making stage.

Conclusions

It is useful to consider the decision to undertake the 30,000 ha project in the range of options which are theoretically conceivable for developing this type of environment.

The option to cultivate rice was different from the others and was chosen not only to respond to the real needs of the Senegalese economy, but also to conform to a tradition which associates rice with tropical alluvial valleys. A stock-raising policy, not as yet carried out, could also have been conceivable: Senegal imports dairy produce and meat. Artificial fertilizers are expensive, but on the other hand, livestock are sent away from this region. The possibilities of a joint agricultural-pastoral project were envisaged only at a later date (IEMVT 1966), but nothing has been attempted in this direction. Intensive stock-raising could have been possible by growing forage crops, used for fattening the Sahel cattle coming from Ferlo or Mauritania. Fishing, or certain types of fish-farming could also have been developed.

The option favouring large-scale operations and colonist communities stems from the idea that this is how to obtain large quantities of surplus goods which could then be sold. The peasants and the stockmen of the region consider the project as an expropriation of their lands. The colonists themselves are not as satisfied as those who benefit from small-scale developments. Since choice is based on deciding what to do first, would it not have been better to first develop a number of the small basins where demographic and emigration problems were particularly acute? It is possible that there would have been more serious land-tenure problems, but the Ronck example shows a possible solution: the public authorities provide a minimal structural basis for development (e.g. an embankment) and supplies technical aid only as desired, so that costs to be borne by the peasants remain within acceptable limits.

PROGRAMME FOR THE DEVELOPMENT OF STOCK-RAISING IN THE MOPTI REGION (MALI)[1]

The Opération de développement de l'élevage dans la Région de Mopti (Programme for the Development of Stock-Raising in the Mopti Region), in the fifth administrative region of Mali, was established following a request for aid made by the Government of Mali to the International Development Association. It covers the period 1975-1979 and its estimated cost is 15.3 million dollars. This is the largest project for developing stock-raising ever financed in Africa. Three natural regions are found in the administrative Region of Mopti:
- the Niger interior delta, a vast plain traversed by the Niger River and its tributaries, covered by floodwaters from July to December, and providing after flood retreat rich pastures (*bourgou*) and innumerable watering places (the river, lakes, ponds, pools);
- the Bandiagara Plateau, a block of solid sandstone;
- the Eastern Séno-Gondo and Gourma plains lying inside the loop of the Niger.

From a pastoral point of view, these three regions should be considered as a whole. With some differences in the exact times, most of the livestock carry out the same pattern of transhumance: in the dry season they gather in the pastures uncovered by the retreat of the floodwaters; during the rainy season, after the floods, they disperse to the peripheral regions as they are attracted to the new flush of green pasture and the numerous water points in the Gourma and Séno-Gondo. A small part of the livestock of this region does not follow these movements back and forth but remains in Gourma and Gondo during the dry season.

Programme justification and objectives

It can be noted that, during the last decade, there has been an increasing interest in projects for developing stock-raising. The most numerous and expensive projects concern the setting up of ranches, ranching being defined as 'rational, large-scale cattle-breeding on natural grasslands, the land being fenced off and divided into vast parks allowing rotation of pasture, fire control, animal selection and monitoring of health' (Marty and Robinet 1966). In the Sahel zone, such ranches were created or planned at Doli in Senegal, Kaédi in Mauritania, Niono in Mali, Toukounous and Sanam in Niger, Ouadi Rimé in Chad. The second type of project consists in growing forage crops with the help of pumping stations or wells, usually accompanied by zootechnical supervision and various structures for marketing the produce. The growing interest in stock-raising can be attributed to various factors:
- economic valorization of products related to stock-raising due to town expansion and the increasing demand of the coastal countries;
- degradation of rangeland through overgrazing, aggravated by the 1969-73 drought; the increase in herd size precludes veterinary care, especially in relation to the campaign against the rinder pest, as the increase in numbers is not being compensated by sufficient sales.

In Mali, stock-raising is an essential sector of the economy, representing 22 per cent of the gross national product and providing half of the country's exports. Compared to the rest of the region, the Niger interior delta provides exceptional conditions for stock-raising. This explains why the Foulani, traditionally stockmen, were gradually attracted to this area from the 14th century onwards. They had a predominant historical and cultural rôle, especially in the 19th century, when the Foulani Empire gave this region its distinctive character through Islam and its political organization. The Foulani are now the most numerous of the ethnic groups in this region, comprising about 350,000 of the 950,000 inhabitants of the administrative region. The cattle in this region represent more than a quarter of the total national livestock (30 per cent). The Mopti and Gao regions are the best cattle areas of Mali. In these areas, better conditions for developing cattle-raising prevail, namely less pronounced climatic drought and considerable resources of surface water and pasture. Two other reasons can be noted, which are political rather than economic in nature. The Mopti Region already benefits from

1. Programme financed by IBRD, the International Bank for Reconstruction and Development. The comments which follow are those of J. Gallais, who served as a consultant during the preparation of the programme, and do not necessarily reflect the opinions of the IBRD.

projects to develop rice and millet cultivation and fishing. The stockmen are therefore asking that something be done for them, and even more so as other types of development, such as the extension of paddyfields, can eventually hinder traditional stock-raising.

In addition, the geographical situation of the Mopti Region means it has an important central position with respect to Mali and the neighbouring nations. Mopti is a link between the most highly developed regions of Mali (Bamako Region, Office du Niger) and the Sahara-Sahel regions. The Mopti Region also shares frontiers with Upper Volta and Mauritania, and the stockmen traditionally ignore the frontiers to take advantage of the various facilities they can find. A boost in the pastoral economy of the Fifth Region means that emigration will decline and eventually that other stockmen will be attracted to the region.

'To build up and improve the livestock of the region, to render it safe from drought', is the objective to be reached by the following measures:
- classical zootechnical interventions (increased health control, experiments, training of stockmen);
- encouragement of sales by setting up several markets and a modern slaughter house;
- education, especially teaching the stockmen to read and write in accordance with their needs;
- use of education, regulations and various technical facilities to control stock-raising activities via the 'constitution of stock-raising communities', the most original and ambitious element of the project.

Thus an attempt is made to develop stock-raising on a small scale by controlling the activities of two distinct but complementary ecological units: the Niger interior delta and its periphery. As soon as possible after flood retreat, the stockmen who have settled on the periphery or in the delta itself bring in their herds of cattle. Soon afterwards the semi-sedentary and nomadic stockmen also bring in their cattle, as they too wish to fatten their animals on the flood retreat pastures. These people have fields and homes in the periphery regions where only old people and a few dairy cows remain. During the last decades, the numbers of animals which congregate in the delta have been increasing with the addition of herds which formerly stayed outside the delta during the dry season, and through the decline of the traditional regulations which spaced out the use of flood-retreat

pastures. Pastures have also been reduced because of the extension of rice cultivation. Studies show that the carrying capacity of the land has been surpassed and that degradation has begun. The flood-retreat pastures should be less heavily grazed, but, on the other hand, certain rangelands on the periphery of the delta are underexploited, firstly due to the lack of watering places, and secondly to the preference for using the delta pastures. An equal distribution of grazing between the delta and the peripheral regions can be obtained only if a policy is adopted for managing the water resources, and if the stockmen accept some regulation of their grazing practices. Indeed, the programme plans to sink 70 wells and dig 50 water-holes on the return itineraries in order to encourage the stockmen to delay going to the delta and to keep some livestock in the peripheral regions.

In the first phase of the programme for medium scale development, it is hoped to rationalize pasture utilization by:
- creating a series of water points in the peripheral regions, the locality and density of which will be determined by the carrying capacity;
- restoring the traditional routes for trans-humance and the traditional stopping places in the delta, thus gradually allowing use of the *bourgou*.

In the second phase, the Region is to be sub-divided into Development Units more or less adapted to the pattern of pasture utilization and to the number of water holes.

With respect to large-scale development, the programme plans a first experimental phase, consisting of the creation of 'stock-raising communities' in which 10 to 50 families owning 200 to 1,000 heads of cattle will have exclusive rights to 2,000 to 10,000 ha of land dotted with watering places. They will be asked to manage their pastures more rationally through rotation of grazing, limitation of numbers of livestock, respect of health control measures, maintenance of water-points, plantation and conservation of forage-bearing trees.

The ODEM, the Opération de développement de l'élevage dans la Région de Mopti (Project for Development of Stock-Raising in the Mopti Region), part of the Ministry of Production, is responsible for these activities. The head-quarters of this service is at Mopti, beside the experimental station.

Choosing options

There is considerable knowledge about this region. The hydrology (Auvray 1960), populations and economy (Missoes 1961) of the Niger interior delta have been studied and a regional analysis has also been made (Gallais 1967). The geology of the neighbouring regions is well studied (Defossez 1962; Reichelt 1972), but the analysis of the human environment is not as comprehensive as that of the interior delta and was in any case published after decisions were already taken. Some more data has been obtained by various studies undertaken for this project financed by the FAC (Fonds d'aide et de coopération): study on grasses (Boudet 1972); herd studies (Coulomb 1972), socio-economic studies (SEDES 1972); but, as these studies provide a justification for the project and propose the concrete measures to be taken, they can hardly question the principle behind the development project as a whole. The project does, however, seem to be backed up by national, regional and local justifications as well as by public opinion. Nevertheless, it can be discussed in terms of a choice of objectives and methods.

The main objective is to build up the livestock which has suffered an estimated 25 per cent loss, and to increase the number of animals to 1,540,000 in 1981, a figure which corresponds to the regional carrying capacity. In 1973, there were 1,230,000 heads of cattle, which, without the project, would have risen to 1,390,000. Each family should own 20 cattle with 5 to 10 smaller animals, yielding an annual income of 100,000 Mali francs ($200) instead of the 65,000 francs which would have been earned without the project. From the point of view of public finances, this project will run at a loss because it is partially financed by the State. The essential aim therefore is to moderately increase the number of livestock to the stockmen's advantage. The risks involved are the following:
- The carrying capacity can suddenly be reduced by another drought (the time interval between exceptional droughts is unknown).
- It is not certain whether the increase in herd size will result in an increase in family income, and whether there be sufficient initiative to reduce numbers by selling the older animals and the surplus calves. The project tends to make the stockmen specialize in breeding young animals, especially in the peripheral region. Although it is less expensive to produce calves by extensive Sahel-type stock-raising, it is not sure that the stockmen of this region will choose to breed more young animals.

Another option would have been to go over completely to breeding calves. However, this would have come up against other difficulties: the regions which specialize in fattening animals may not offer sufficient openings, and although the Bandiagara Plateau and the Ségou region buy up young animals, they may not be able to greatly increase their buying capacity. As the cattle are driven to market on hoof, sales are limited to the peripheral regions. The final fattening of cattle could have been ensured by specialized units (special ranches, feedlots), but these projects were not adopted in the final programme. These would have taken up land used for traditional stock-raising and would have thus raised a considerable amount of opposition from the stockmen, for whom the whole programme would have become suspect. The economic objectives of the programme are therefore moderate, designed to be of direct benefit to the stockmen without creating sudden changes in the organizational structures. However, the success of these objectives does depend on variables that are difficult to control.

The project considers the Séno-Mango peripheral area situated to the East of the administrative Region as a particular stock-raising area, whose development will help to equally distribute grazing activities and reduce pressure on the interior delta. Water and grass resources are relatively well studied, and it is proposed to sink 60 wells. Figures for herd size and total population are only approximate. There would be a risk of underexploiting the wells, which the project will try to avoid by installing them gradually over time. As for where the wells should be sunk, there is a choice of wells serving livestock placed in the midst of pastures, or else village wells. The stockmen winter their animals far away from the villages and come back in the dry season. Constructing wells for livestock would mean that the stockmen would not return to the villages, which would deprive them of their traditional exchange of goods and services with the peasants. In addition, the region is gradually being cultivated as a result of immigration of the Dogon peasants, and this spread of cultivation is only limited by a lack of wells. It is therefore possible that peasant farmers will settle around the wells built for the stockmen. What will the stockmen think then? The setting up of responsible and organized stock-raising communities will help to avoid the peasants' gradually pushing the stockmen away from their wells, as was sometimes the case in the Ferlo in Senegal. The risk does remain, and if this situation were to come about, it would be impossible to carry out organized stock-raising activities as planned.

The overall strategy is to reduce pressure on the delta by developing the peripheral regions. The Séno-Mango development will hardly contribute to this objective because it is an independent stock-raising region where the majority of stockmen do not frequent the delta. The question can thus be raised as to whether a large amount of the project's budget devoted to the Séno-Mango will not seriously cut back other measures which would contribute towards this redistribution. Such measures would be the construction of about 20 ponds on the return itineraries to the East of the delta, and about 20 ponds and 10 wells on the itineraries leading back to the West of the delta. Another possible, but more ambitious, option of this type would have been to construct a dense network of ponds.

In the delta itself, the options taken are very limited: creation of an experimental station to study the methods of pasture regeneration, which are then to be tested in two neighbouring villages. The natural and human environments are in fact so particular that it is not known exactly how to go about modernizing stock-raising in the delta. The first phase of the 1975-79 project will perhaps allow closer study of what methods can be used. Different options can be envisaged according to the amount of ODEM intervention.

- The ODEM creates ranches, fattening stations, feedlot areas, etc., which can be situated in the low-lying plains where natural pasture is richest. Through rotation of pastures, higher yields could be obtained than with the traditional system. These structures could be placed on some of the higher plains with poor, lightly-grazed pastures. This would then involve forage production using irrigation, a measure which has never been attempted on a large scale in the Sahel.
- The ODEM does not take over any land traditionally used for stock-raising, but firmly controls these activities through very strict ruling of grazing density and timing. This involves dividing the land up into sections, marking out each area in the field, drawing up a timetable which annually adjusts grazing-times to fit flood characteristics, and continuously checking the various activities by public services or the administrations of stock-raising communities. This option would have to be based on a considerable amount of preliminary study, a permanent dialogue with the

stockmen, and the existence of a substantial land registry unit at the ODEM.
- The ODEM tries to develop cultivating adapted forage crops for each stock-raising village. This would help to build up herds of stall-fed dairy cows in places where milk could be collected at a reasonable cost. These herds (*dounti*) exist in the traditional system but consist of only a few cows. Besides the spread of adapted forage crops, this option leads to organizing milk collection and eventually to an industrial enterprise (e.g. manufacture of condensed milk, which Mali imports in large quantities). This option also necessitates various zootechnical measures related to the stall-feeding of animals (construction of simple cow-sheds, parasite control, etc.).

The Programme de développement de l'élevage dans la Région de Mopti (Programme for the Development of Stock-Raising in the Mopti Region) involves two fundamental options:

The first is through taxation. Any attempt at rationalizing stock-raising must control the numbers of livestock. Is this control compatible with the taxes that are currently imposed on cattle? Several choices are possible:
- abolish the present taxation system and replace it with taxes corresponding to the services received (vaccinations, use of grazing zones, etc.);
- regulate taxes according to the project's objectives, for example if it is wished to promote dairy farming, the village stall-fed herd of cows could be exempt from tax; if it is wished to change the herd age-structure, taxes could be graded by age (a technique of marking animals could easily be developed in order to facilitate verification).

The second concerns economic aspects. The project is based on utilizing the currently available pastures through grazing of livestock of the region. However, the pastures could be reduced by increased cropping; what then is the relationship between the stock-raising development project and other developments, particularly rice cultivation? All these projects come under the responsibility of the Ministry of Production, but are there any structures for integrating projects on the regional level? Which is the option for distributing land amongst the various sectors of the economy? A master-plan for regional land-use would be necessary to integrate the various projects in their present forms and during their future development.

In conclusion, one cannot yet measure all the consequences of the Programme de développement de l'élevage dans la Région de Mopti, but it does pose many problems concerning options, most of are linked. Some problems have already been identified, but others have not yet been envisaged.

IV. CONCLUSIONS

A few case studies have brought out the essential characteristic of the traditional strategies of the Sudan-Sahel zone: matching food security with village ideology. It is true that since 1950, these two concerns have become less important, but they are still fundamental to this society. Food security is still the primordial objective as long as the Sudan-Sahel zone remains enclaved, far away from the main axes of communication and out of reach of the major exchange routes; the 1969-74 drought dramatically demonstrated that the problem had not been solved. Village ideology has been worn down, more so in the real Sahel area (Gallais 1975), but social life continues to be based on ties and links which are expressed in concrete terms by the village itself.

Most development projects have a single purpose. Within the context of a national strategy, they tend to develop a particular type of production on a regional basis. This procedure is in contradiction with the traditional strategy for food security, in that it attempts to liberate the surplus saleable food products (millet, cattle) or else to expand indirect food crops (ground-nuts, cotton), to the detriment of food producing activities. The Sudan-Sahel people, more or less voluntary participants in such development projects, are constantly redirecting some of their efforts, their time and their land towards production along traditional lines. This tendency can be seen even in newly settled agricultural areas offering the attractive perspective of cash crops (Office du Niger and the 30,000 ha Project).

This contradiction is particularly felt with respect to agriculture and stock-raising. The Sudan-Sahel peoples have a mixed farming and stock-raising civilization. Peasants and stockmen try to associate fields and livestock either in an integrated system, or through various interactions between ethnic groups. The case studies of the Zarma, Dogon and Ouolof peoples have shown that acquiring cattle was considered a means of storing food. Development projects are usually lacking in this respect; agricultural development projects ignore, and all too often eliminate, stock-raising and the stockmen. Exceptions are rare; one of the positive features of the Office du Niger is to have allowed and encouraged the colonists to develop peasant stock-raising. In the same way, development projects in favour of stock-raising have hardly ever managed to integrate agriculture. In the Southern Ferlo (Senegal), the low-lying pastures should have been a focus for both agricultural and stock-raising activities: indeed, fields have been set up in this area, but these make it more and more difficult to exploit the forage resources. It is extremely difficult to design and conduct a development project that really integrates agriculture and stock-raising, whereas single-purpose projects appear to be much simpler, giving relatively higher chances of success within a given time. In the Sudan-Sahel zone, these single-purpose projects represent 'technological transfers': the projects for developing agriculture are inspired by Southern Sahel examples. The particular dual-purpose economy - agriculture and stock-raising - characteristic of this Sudan-Sahel zone is not sufficiently taken into consideration.

The second point where many development projects and traditional strategies conflict concerns the pattern of human land-use. Development projects in Africa are based on existing administrative structures - region or province, departments or counties, sections or subdivisions, districts, villages - which implies that these different areas have a geographical, demographic and social unity which they are far from possessing in reality. Projects often fail when it is decided to make a whole region or department produce more ground-nuts, for example, using the same techniques everywhere and the same means of gaining local support, without considering the particular characteristics of the natural environment or of social conditions. Imposing a bureaucratic organization on geographical patterns means that regional characteristics are lost, the same characteristics on which the traditional strategies are founded. These considerations are valid for all areas, but, on the village level, Sudan-Sahel societies are not confined to village settlements as are certain Sudan societies further South. It has been noted that the people are not rigidly fixed in one place.

For the Dogon people this has given rise to two types of villages; for the Zarma, a vast territory characterized by social distinctions; for the Rimaïbé of the Niger interior delta, paddyfields laid out according to the irregularity of floods; and for the Ouolof of the *oualo*, commercial exchange and use of resources beyond the river frontier. Thus in the Sudan-Sahel zone, the villages are open to passing influences whilst maintaining the intrinsic way of life. Bureaucratic organization and development projects ignore and frequently come up against this unstable equilibrium, specific to each group of people.

Setting up colonist villages is a delicate operation, even in the case of the 30,000 ha Project, where an attempt has been made to achieve a certain unity through the grouping of people with similar ethnic and geographical origins. Rather than superimpose a new village organization, would it not be better to include development projects in the overall communal village plan?

To consider a village an administrative unit on which to base development projects is to assume that the village has a certain community life, institutional framework, authorities and a strategy, at a different scale, be it a wider or a more limited one. It is therefore necessary to carry out a careful inventory on a case-by-case basis, particularly when the people considered have a long tradition of stock-raising and are only recently and incompletely settled in villages. The Programme de développement de l'élevage dans la Région de Mopti had amongst its objectives 'the constitution of stock-raising communities', and it would thus be regrettable to consider all the officially recognized Foulani villages as valid for this type of development.

Modern decision-making can ignore these problems in the name of national economic interest or of an ideological objective. To do so, there must be the means and the will to overcome traditional strategies. Modern decision-making can also be harmonized with collective strategies not entirely of a traditional nature. It is therefore necessary to have a clear understanding of the basic divergences between strategies and the possible compromises which can be made.

BIBLIOGRAPHY

AUBREVILLE, A. 1950. *Flore forestière soudano-guinéenne. A.O.F. Cameroun. A.E.F.* Société d'Editions Géographiques maritimes et coloniales, Paris.

AUVRAY, C. 1960. *Monographie du Niger, B. La cuvette lacustre.* ORSTOM, Paris.

BONNET-DUPEYRON, M.F. 1951. *Cartes de l'élevage pour le Sénégal et la Mauritanie.* ORSTOM, Paris.

BOUDET, G. 1972. *Projet de développement de l'élevage dans la région de Mopti (République du Mali). Etude agrostologique.* Institut d'Elevage et de Médecine vétérinaire des pays tropicaux, Maisons-Alfort.

BOUTILLIER, J.L.; CANTRELLE, P.; CAUSSE, J.; LAURENT, C.; N'DOYE, Th. 1962. *La moyenne vallée du Sénégal. Etude socio-économique.* Presses universitaires de France, Paris.

COULOMB, J. 1972. *Projet de développement de l'élevage dans la région de Mopti (République du Mali). Etude du troupeau.* Institut d'Elevage et de Médecine vétérinaire des pays tropicaux, Maisons-Alfort.

DEFOSSEZ, M. 1962. *Contributions à l'étude géologique et hydrogéologique de la Boucle du Niger.* Bureau de Recherches géologiques et minières, Paris.

DIOP, A. 1960. Enquête sur la migration toucouleur à Dakar. *Bulletin IFAN*, série B, 22, p. 393-418.

GADEN, H. 1935. Du régime des terres de la vallée du Sénégal au Fouta antérieurement à l'occupation française. *Bull. du Comité d'Etudes historiques et scientifiques de l'A.O.F.*, 4, p. 403-414.

GALLAIS, J. 1965. Le paysan dogon (République du Mali). *Les Cahiers d'Outre-Mer*, 70, p. 123-143.

GALLAIS, J. 1967. *Le Delta intérieur du Niger : Etude de géographie régionale.* IFAN, Dakar.

GALLAIS, J. 1975. *Pasteurs et paysans du Gourma. La condition sahélienne.* Mémoires du Centre d'Etudes de géographie tropicale. Centre national de la Recherche scientifique, Paris.

HERVOUET, J.P. 1971. *Les éleveurs riziculteurs du Moyen-Delta du Sénégal (les Peuls et l'aménagement).* Mémoire de maîtrise, Université de Dakar.

INSTITUT D'ELEVAGE ET DE MEDECINE VETERINAIRE DES PAYS TROPICAUX (IEMVT). 1966. *Etude des pâturages naturels et des problèmes pastoraux dans le Delta du Sénégal. Définition d'une politique de l'élevage.* Secrétariat d'Etat aux Affaires étrangères chargé de la coopération, Paris.

LERICOLLAIS, A.; VERNIERE, M. 1975. L'émigration toucouleur; du fleuve Sénégal à Dakar. *Cahiers ORSTOM, série Sciences humaines*, 12, N° 2, p. 161-176.

MARTY, J.P.; ROBINET, A.H. 1966. *Le ranching, pôle de développement du monde pastoral sahélien.* Secrétariat d'Etat aux Affaires étrangères chargé de la coopération, Paris.

MISSION SOCIO-ECONOMIQUE DU SOUDAN (MISSOES). 1961. *L'alimentation des populations rurales du Delta vif du Niger et de l'Office du Niger.* Ministère de la Coopération et Institut national de la statistique et des études économiques (INSEE), Paris.

NICOLAS, G. 1962. Un village Bonzou du Niger. Etude d'un terroir. *Les Cahiers d'Outre-Mer*, 58, p. 138-165.

PAPY, L. 1951. La vallée du Sénégal. *Les Cahiers d'Outre-Mer*, 16, p. 1-48.

PELISSIER, P. 1966. *Les paysans du Sénégal. Les civilisations agraires du Cayor à la Casamance.* Imprimerie Fabrègue, Saint-Yrieix.

PORTERES, R. 1950. Vieilles agricultures de l'Afrique intertropicale. Centres d'origine et de diversification variétale primaire et berceaux d'agriculture antérieurs au 16e siècle. *L'Agronomie tropicale*, 15, N° 9-10, p. 489-506.

RAVAULT, F. 1964. Kanel. L'exode rural dans un village de la vallée du Sénégal. *Les Cahiers d'Outre-Mer*, 65, p. 58-80.

REICHELT, R. 1972. *Géologie du Gourma (Afrique occidentale). Un seuil et un bassin du Précambien supérieur.* Bureau de Recherches géologiques et minières, Paris.

RICHARD-MOLARD, J. 1949. *Afrique occidentale française.* Berger-Levrault, Paris.

SIDIKOU, A.H. 1974. Sédentarité et mobilité entre Niger et Zgaret. *Etudes nigériennes*, 34.

SOCIETE D'ETUDES POUR LE DEVELOPPEMENT ECONOMIQUE ET SOCIAL (SEDES). 1972. *Projet de développement de l'élevage dans la région de Mopti. Rapport de synthèse.* SEDES, Paris.

TOUPET, C. 1966. *Etude du milieu physique du Massif de l'Assaba (Mauritanie).* IFAN, Dakar.

VIDAL, M. 1935. Etude sur la tenure des terres indigènes au Fouta. *Bull. du Comité d'Etudes historiques et scientifiques de l'A.O.F.* 4, p. 415-448.

Traditional strategies, modern decision-making and management of natural resources in Sudan Africa

P. Pélissier and S. Diarra

I. ENVIRONMENTAL LIMITATIONS AND HUMAN CONDITIONS

Tropical Africa is usually divided by comparing the distribution of the major civilizations with climatic and biogeographic zones. This shall not be attempted here, but it is clear that the Sudan savannas of Africa are in fact characterized by similar ecological limiting factors, a fairly comparable history and also similar types of response to economic and population pressure. Here, discussion will be limited to those aspects which might help explain the ancient and contemporary strategies that man has used to manage, master or develop the natural resources of interest to him.

The Sudan savannas cannot be precisely delimited by a set of isohyets. Fixing the minimal rainfall at 600 or 750 mm does not account for the variations between years that are characteristic of all parts of Africa, variations which are the source of risks and insecurity in agriculture dependent on rainfall. This is the case in Black Africa, where irrigation was practically unknown to traditional civilizations, and even today is exceptional, limited to a few areas managed with modern techniques. Irregularity in the timing and amount of rainfall, although having much less dramatic consequences than in the Sahel, is still a permanent factor affecting Sudan agriculture, and has very many repercussions on farming activities. Thus peasants tend to systematically sow as soon as possible much larger areas than they could even maintain if the rains were sufficiently abundant and favourably distributed throughout the growing season. It is even more difficult to fix the limits between the Sudan savannas and the rain forests or the Guinea savannas, which sometimes lie between the two. This limit is generally taken around isohyet 1,500 mm; it is, however, the distribution of rainfall throughout the year, rather than the total amount, which appears to be the significant factor.

In the Sudan zone, the essential climatic factor to which agriculture must adapt is the sharp contrast between dry and rainy seasons. The latter can last from five to six months. The difference between the two periods is made even greater by the desiccating Eastern wind, the harmattan, which is caused by Saharan high pressures, and which, in the dry season, burns its way across all Sudan Africa. Whatever their aspirations or form of organization, savanna societies arrange the year's activities after the contrasting seasons. There is a frantically busy rainy season devoted to farming, and a dry season free from essential agricultural work and traditionally spent developing the local social life, with movements and exchanges between people.

It is obvious that this severe climatic pattern is the essential factor governing vegetation, whether the climax associations, secondary formations or cultivated plants. However, there can hardly be a more misleading formula than 'savanna', a term which is even more ambiguous than the vegetation to which it refers. It should be noted that this tree-dotted landscape with rhizome-bearing grasses, swept every year by fire and the realm *par excellence* of large herbivores, is not specific to the Sudan zone. On the contrary, the purest, most typical savannas of the geography books are found under equatorial-type climates. Therefore there is no zonal savanna corresponding to the Sudan climatic zone. On the other hand, there is a Sudan vegetation zone characterized by dry forest, which imperceptively decreases in density until it is replaced by the grassy savanna. In fact, this latter vegetation is never completely devoid of trees, even in its most undisturbed forms. Indeed, another ambiguity is that savanna and grassy lands totally devoid of trees tend to be grouped together, and, in consequence, a Sudan zone where trees are absent is not considered as part of the forest zone.

Unesco, 1978. *Management of natural resources in Africa: traditional strategies and modern decision-making.* (MAB Technical Notes 9).

A particularly significant difference can be noted if one flies northwards in a straight line from Abidjan. One flies first over the evergreen forest and the Guinea savannas which cover the Baoulé V mosaic made up of the contrasting forests (tree canopies in the valleys and dense stands on the hills and the tops of slopes), and of vast stretches of grass dotted with fan palms. The structure and the type of vegetation then rapidly change. Above the latitude of Katiola, the whole landscape is covered with tree associations, no longer the stratified and apparently uniform forests of the South, but physionomically homogeneous stands of deciduous trees which change with the seasons and with the density of human occupation.

The most common natural plant formation of the 'Sudan savannas' is in fact a dry forest which is found in dense climax associations as secondary formations - open forests or thick coppices - or else as decimated stands evolving either towards a grassy savanna, or, more often, to park landscapes. These plant associations have been highly modified by man. It is still true that, for Sudan societies, the initial environmental limitation is the clearing of the vigorous forest cover made up of quickly resprouting species that are remarkably adapted to seasonal drought and a long history of periodic fires. Fire, repeated over thousands of years, is always associated with the degeneration of the dry forest and the spread of herbaceous plant formations which are favoured by the destruction of the forest cover.

In addition, when the dry forest is systematically and repetitively cleared, the process of savanization starts to progress at an alarming rate. If man eliminates all forest regrowth, he must then fight against savanna encroachment in order to master the land he is so eager to use. The whole strategy of land-clearing is directed by the risk of savanna encroachment. It constitutes the most important element hindering agricultural development and necessitates ploughing techniques that strictly limit field size. In the same way, the amount of weeding that is necessary appears to be a considerable obstacle preventing the extension of farms and fields, and also the possibility of an increase in productivity of the agricultural workmen. Then again the abandon and periodic shifting of fields is largely dictated by the difficulty in arresting savanna encroachment through manual agriculture, since the Sudan peasant considers that the natural forest fallow is the least expensive and most efficient means to combat weeds.

In contrast to the climatic zones to the North and South, the Sudan zone seems in general to be an area of water dispersal, made up of mostly low plateaux broken up here and there by rugged uplands. There are no ranges of inaccessible mountains but rather immense strechies of well-drained land surrounded by steep ledges, sometimes huge sandstone tables bordered with impressive cliffs. Elsewhere there are rugged hills formed by the remains of ancient eroded blocks. These broken secondary mountains never form complete natural barriers but have become ecological niches and human refuges. Owing to its topography, the nature of its bedrock and its latitude, agriculture in Sudan Africa is faced mainly with relatively poor soils, certainly less rich and more fragile than the soils of the Quaternary ergs which cover most of the Sahel. On the other hand, Sudan Africa is the area par excellence of bowal, i.e. large areas of hard pan which, when scoured by erosion, form sterile slabs as impermeable to water as to the roots of plants. It is one of the greatest of paradoxes that the purest form of African peasant farming is found in an area of either hard pan or sandstone tables, or else of gravelly soils or granitic sands. Only a few uplands of schists and greenstone currently undergoing active weathering offer soils of any interest. There are no vast stretches of alluvial soils as there are in the major Sudan-Sahel valleys, but there are depressions lined with compact clays which are alternatively dried up or saturated, which traditional techniques have generally been unable to develop. It is difficult to find another area where techniques have had such a decisive rôle in differentiating the environment.

One of the environmental limitations that is specific to Sudan Africa is due to the fact that the river valleys are marginal areas for agriculture. This is true only for valleys that are narrow ravines swept by seasonal torrents, but also for wide meandering valleys that drain the low plateaux and are covered with sandy-clay or clay alluviums, which are agronomically more fertile than the gravel or the sands of the neighbouring lands lying between rivers.

Of all the historical and technological reasons which help to explain why the Sudan valleys are so uninhabited, there is one that is overriding: the terrible danger of onchocerciasis or river blindness. The Sudan savannas are hyperendemic foci of this disease, because of their central rôle in water dispersal, due to the fact that they comprise the upper section of the drainage network where river gradients are greatest. Indeed infection is not linked with climate but with the river profile and therefore with the speed of waterflow. The parasitic insect larva is a species of Diptera whose larva can only develop in highly oxygen-ated water, i.e. when water is well mixed by the turbulent flow caused by breaks of slope, rocky sills, banks of sandstone or hard pan, and artificial dams, etc. Repeated infeçtion, as can occur when men work near breeding grounds of this disease, has a disastrous ef-fect on the health and the working capacity of the population, since in its most serious state, it affects the eyes and eventually causes blindness. Thus in many places along the Sudan rivers there are immense strips of uncultivated alluvial land (about 6 million hectares in the Volta basin alone), and the village people who venture there are severely affected. Here and there along the Ghana-Upper Volta frontier, more than 10 per cent of the people are blind and the whole area's activi-ties are influenced by this infection. As blindness does not occur before a certain level of infection by the Microfilaria larva which is not reached before a certain age, if 10 per cent of the people are blind, this effectively represents 30 per cent of the active popula-tion. The populations of Bahr-el-Ghazal in Southern Sudan are probably afflicted to the same extent.

In western Africa, onchocerciasis control is the object of unprecedented international effort, the technique adopted being the eradi-cation of the larval vectors by spraying chem-ical larvicides on water which might harbour the infection. However, the disease will not be totally eliminated before several decades. Onchocerciasis remains the most important lim-itation that confronts the Sudan peasant. Un-like sleeping sickness, which for a long time was present in the tall rain forest, this disease is not reduced by intensive land clear-ing, and many observers believe that, on the contrary, it has spread even more since the beginning of the century (notably through the increase in the number of small dams whose torrential weirs provide potential breeding sites for infection). Onchocerciasis is one of the reasons why people are crowded onto the plateaux in densely populated regions, and in consequence, explains all the impacts of over-exploitation of often mediocre or fragile soils where agriculture is still totally dependent on rainfall. The negative influence of oncho-cerciasis is confirmed even by the exception of the Logone River valley, which lies in the Sudan zone upriver from Bongor, and which, up to just beyond Moundou, has the highest rural

population densities of Chad. Here, the low river gradient and the sometimes hesitating waterflow make this part of the river unsuitable as breeding sites for the Diptera sandflies. In short, one of the most distinctive features of the Sudan zone is the non-utilization of the river valleys (onchocerciasis is, of course, only one of the causes, but probably the most direct). In contrast to the rôle they have had and continue to have in the Sahel, here, river valleys have served as neither highways for trade, centres for settlement, nor geographical bases for land-use patterns. The distribution of the present population and the type of prob-lems that they face are the best illustration of the historical and economic insignificance of the Sudan rivers and their valleys.

Uneven population distribution is very typical of all Black Africa, but nowhere are there such contrasts between underpopulated zones and densely and even overpopulated areas as in the Sudan savannas. Western Africa in particular is literally dotted with islands of high population density, which go from the swamps of the Atlantic coast right up to the mountains of North Cameroun. Against a back-ground of general underpopulation, all the States making up Sudan Africa possess areas where the population is crowded to the point where rational management and development of natural resources are faced with the obstacles that are usually linked with overpopulation, i.e. a disequilibrium between the available resources of a given environment and the re-quirements of the people who live there.

The limitations which arise from population pressure have two major consequences. Firstly, the most remarkable forms of intensive agri-culture and the most original types of land management of Black Africa have been instigated. Secondly, a high rate of rural emigration from certain regions of the Sudan zone has been generated. The first of these consequences will be discussed later in examining the traditional strategies of environmental management. As for the second, it will be sufficient to take Fouta-Djallon and the Mossi area as illustrations. The first area cannot support the 50 to 80 inhab-itants/km^2 who live in the central plateau of the Guinea highlands. The Foula people of Fouta-Djallon therefore colonize the foothill savannas up to Haute-Casamance, but more frequently emigrate to the towns on the coast, Dakar, Conakry, and Abidjan. As for the Mossi area, where population densities locally exceed 100 inhabitants/km^2, many people leave to colonize and cultivate the peripheral regions within the Upper Volta frontiers, and there is a high rate of temporary and permanent emigration towards the plantations of Ghana and the Ivory Coast. Here, forest clearing and development are very closely linked with the arrival of a massive labour force of Sudan origin. This emigration brings in indispensable money resources to the areas of departure, and it relieves population pressure and the associated list of difficulties concerning food, land-tenure and social matters. However, this emigration greatly retards any possibilities of developing these areas as, above all, it affects the adult male population. As a result, recent investigations have noted that since 1960, emigration has practically stopped population increase in the Mossi area and has even relieved the pressure of overpopulation on the lands of the Western Mossi territory, i.e. the Ouahigouya and Koudougou regions (Rémy 1968). In these same regions, however, emigration of the working population has reached exodus proportions since 45 per cent of the men between 15 and 45 of age have left (Kohler 1972). It thus becomes very difficult for the population to continue and, even more so, to improve their farming activities, and this problem also jeopardizes any progress using technical innovations. Paradoxically, renovation of overpopulated zones is very often handicapped for the following reasons: there are insufficient manual workers; the chiefs of the farming communities are cut off from the outside world; the majority of adults are relatively old, and the inactive age classes are becoming an excessive burden on the society as a whole. For example, in the Mossi area, for every 100 active men in 1973, there were 132 women and 242 'inactive' inhabitants (old people and children). These are average figures which do not account for the extreme situation where the ratio of both the inactive plus the female population over the productive male population can be above 400 per cent.

These contrasting population densities are the result of historical events, although they have become worse due to the modern population explosion. There are also historical reasons explaining why some areas are empty and others overpopulated, why vast areas have been abandoned and why other sites, with hardly any more natural resources to their advantage, are crowded with settlements. The Sudan savannas are full of examples of regions which have been abandoned through the course of history. This is the case of the sparsely populated zone (less than 10 and often less than 5 inhabitant/km^2) which runs from the Bénoué River valley and the West of Mid-Nigeria (depopulated through Fulani raids) up to the banks of the Upper Bandama River (Ivory Coast). This zone crosses the dry forests of Benin and Mid-Togo which are marked by the Abomey wars, the underpopulated lands of Central Ghana which for a long time were devastated by slave expeditions, and the wooded savannas of the North-East Ivory Coast where to this day, population is sparser than before the Samory campaigns. Historical events, more ancient and less well known, are also responsible for the zones of high population density. Roughly speaking, one can distinguish two major types of densely populated zones whose origins and organizations have different explanations. Firstly, there are the refuges where men have grouped together for survival, which have become increasingly crowded as there was insufficient land available to absorb the growing population. Secondly, there are zones where high population density is the result of a political power which was able to control land-use activities. This difference is not only of historical interest but also forms the basis of a fundamental distinction between the structures, the objectives and the techniques of Sudan societies, and in consequence between their different attitudes in managing and developing the natural resources at their disposal.

The first type of high population density is represented by societies that only managed to keep their identity by shutting themselves off from the world, thus being able to maintain a type of society founded on equality of rights and opportunities for all people whatever their birth or personal development outside any social restrictions, stubborn refusal of any permanent or centralized political organization, and respect of women's place in society. As a result, there are no classes or castes, chiefs or followers. The only permissible social limitations concern lineage and territory, the latter being managed by the elders. In short, these are fervently egalitarian societies which are held together only by family ties. These ties are strong enough to make a really united community, the only true counterbalance to a refusal of all authority and of all kinds of restrictive structures. One can distinguish two levels of organization of these egalitarian peasant farming societies, indicated by a different lay-out of the houses. Most often, the societies where lineage is important and political power relatively unimportant have a dispersed pattern of settlement. Each family farm, sometimes organized as a small fort (as is today the Dagari-le-Yir land concession (Savannet 1970)), is established on its own lands and, with other farms, often makes an indefinite pattern which has no pole for social, economic or administrative matters. The 'village' is therefore a completely alien concept applied by the outside world, which has no basis in the traditional society other than its members uniting to combat natural enemies and external dangers. This is the case of the Diola, Balant and Baga rice-growers hidden away in the mangroves and on the off-shore bars of the Rivières du Sud coast, the mountain peoples of the Monts du Mandara in North Cameroun, the Somba farmers settled on the slopes of Atakora in North-Eastern Bénin, and also their Kabyé cousins in the mountains of Northern Togo. The fact that this peasant farming culture has persisted for such a long time and at a distance of thousands of kilometers shows that its social and cultural identity is extremely well founded. It will be seen whether this is also true of their own particular techniques for managing and exploiting natural resources.

There is a second level of organization, less common than the first, which characterizes these peasant farming cultures. These are the peasant farmers who, although they do not belong to any State, have managed to create close-knit village communities while respecting their refusal of all forms of restrictive structure and their ideal of an egalitarian society and personal development. A particularly good example of this type of situation is found in the Bwa country in the West of Upper Volta (Capron 1973). Here, houses are concentrated in the middle of a communal piece of land, and the village forms a veritable city, tightly bound and shut in on itself. This society shows a certain stratification, with blacksmiths and 'griots' placed on the same level as farmers. The territory of each community is usually separated from neighbouring territories by a thick stretch of forest, and the village society safeguards political autonomy as fervently as it rejects any hierarchy other than age and responsibilities given to family chiefs. However, the antiquity, the sedentary nature and the farming techniques of these village communities show that they have attitudes and objectives concerning natural resources that are very similar to those of all paeleo-Sudan civilizations.

There are completely different origins for the structures and the strategies of the peoples in highly populated areas which were created by a political power, whether it was a feudal type or a centralized state type. Moreover, most of these areas result from the imposition of a political and military organization on a more or less long-established paeleo-Sudan people. This was done either by a foreign aristocracy, or else by an influx of

people possessing a social hierarchical ideology, specialized workmen and an administrative structure. Sometimes a minority group, these foreign leaders had the principal task of defending the peasant population. With this protection, these peasant people were not only able to keep their own personality, techniques and values, but were also able to increase their numbers, thus giving rise to areas of high population density where the methods of social organization and the farming techniques have two distinct cultural origins. This is the case of the Sérèr people of Senegal at the North edge of the Sudan zone where the rural population comes from old peasant stock, whereas the political and military hierarchy, which ensured their long-lasting and effective organization, originally comes from Manding aristocracy. Here, however, it is the paeleo-negritic basis which has maintained and imposed its values and its techniques, notably concerning the management and the development of a particularly unproductive environment. Because of this, it has always been able to simultaneously exploit the natural resources and increase population density *in situ*.

Another noteworthy centre of high population density which results from political organization is represented by the Mossi area, in the heart of the Upper Volta plateau. Here, the accumulation of settlements can be explained neither by the rainfall (650-1,000 mm), the quality of the soils (granitic sands or gravelly soils with frequent outcrops of laterite), nor by the system of agricultural production. What made the 'Mossi area', in spite of the mediocrity of the natural resources, is that, from the 14th century onwards, a warrior aristocracy set up a political administrative organization and took over a paeleo-Sudan people having a social structure based on lineage. Supported by administrative institutions and efficient military organization, the Mossi monarchy divided the territory into hierarchical chiefdoms, favoured the development of a society made up of specialized classes added on top of the initial peasant population, and facilitated an increase in population. This latter essentially seems to have resulted from a political system founded on central authority and indifference towards peasant values (Rémy 1968; Kohler 1971). Before the advent of the contemporary increase in population, the high population of the Mossi area resulted from three factors which have influenced all situations of the same type. Firstly, the population was protected against external dangers, either slave raids, foreign invasions (notably the long-lasting threat of invasion by the Foulani) or action taken in the name of the 'holy war'. In spite of the absence of any natural barriers or refuges, the people of the Mossi area managed to increase in numbers during these centuries spent behind the shields of their warriors. Secondly, the Mossi monarchy was generally able to keep internal peace, notably forbidding civil wars, looting and servitude of the inhabitants under their control, thus providing suitable conditions for population growth. Thirdly and lastly, for centuries the large Mossi population was augmented by the numbers of captives taken from neighbouring peoples during defensive wars or expansionist campaigns led by the aristocracy and their warriors. However, the aristocrats' power, force, organization and ability to expand their territory meant that the majority of Mossi people, and first of all their leaders, had to adopt a strategy for using natural resources which was diametrically opposed to that of the paeleo-Sudan peasant cultures. A study of the Haoussa country around Kano and Katsina in North Nigeria, for example, would show that once more, the ancient and effective political structures are at the origin of high population densities, which here have been reinforced by Islam, trade and urban centres. Such a study would also show that these structures form the basis of a veritable expansion of the Haoussa people, whose pioneers have for a long time crossed the present Niger frontier and have pushed agricultural colonization up to the borders of the Sahel.

Finally, the case of the central plateaux of Fouta-Djallon will be mentioned because it is more recent and has a theocratic basis. Here, the uplands surrounded by steep cliffs cut by canyon-like valleys are free from disease and have long undergone savanization because of their altitude. The Foulani people did not use them as refuges but gradually settled there, and in the 18th century took over political power. The Islamic Foulani then subordinated the negroid Dialonké people and divided the central plateau into a series of zones which were in turn divided into administrative conscriptions with a solid military and religious organization (Richard-Molard 1944). The Foulani bastion was therefore constituted of the highest, the most disease-free but also the poorest of plateaux (sandstone blocks and bowé-lateritic crusts). When the chiefs settled down, they accumulated great numbers of servile labourers brought back from expeditions to pagan peoples of the peripheral region, depopulated by the holy war. Thus the most populated cultivated lands in Guinea are also the most unproductive and the least suitable for agriculture. The inhabitants of Fouta-Djallon are brought together by a common religion, culture, organization and also by the bareness of their environment, making this area one of the greatest centres of emigration of Sudan Africa.

All modern strategies concerning the exploitation of natural resources must take a fundamental lesson from this examination of the origins and nature of the contrasts in population density in Sudan Africa. Even today there is no systematic correlation between a poor environment and a sparse population, or between high population densities and a particularly advantageous climate or soil. Unexploited and overexploited lands lie side by side, and the population centres are the result of human decisions and historical events which were, at least originally, largely indifferent to the quality of available natural resources.

Another limitation which influences exploitation of the Sudan environment is the range of possible cultivated plants consistent with climatic conditions and the choice made by the different civilizations. African peasant civilization is fundamentally devoted to the cultivation of cereal crops. Practically everywhere, millet and sorghum are the bases of agricultural systems and there are numerous varieties suited to all types of soil and climate. Only rice, the hardiest varieties of which are also of African origin, are regionally supplanting these crops in the Southern and especially Western fringes of the study area. The supremacy of cereals is only slightly contested by yams in the Southern Sudan savannas, and there again only at the East of the Guinea mountains. Yams need deep soils and rainfall over 1,000 mm. Even though manioc is now grown everywhere and maize cultivation is spreading, these crops are still unimportant. The complete list of food crops is very short, which aggravates scarcities. Although mangoes have been adopted everywhere, proper orchards are rare except for very recent innovations. The list of cash crops is even shorter, these being strictly limited by climate. Only ground-nuts and cotton are possible, the former everywhere where soils are suitable, and cotton only beyond the 1,000 mm isohyet. Animal-raising activities are much more widespread than is usually stated, although there is no real stock-raising as such, with the exceptions of the areas conquered by the Foulani (Foula of Fouta-Djallon, Fulani of North Nigeria, M'Bororo of Central Cameroun). All the paeleo-Sudan peoples raise cattle and, even in the regions where cattle are monopolized by the chiefs, the majority of the population raise smaller livestock. However, natural conditions eliminate zebus beyond the 800 mm isohyet, and the trypanoresistant races such as the N'Dama have very low milk yields. Livestock are considered as social status symbols and a bond of lineage, and are insignificant as a source of food. Their sometimes essential rôle is much more closely related to the analysis of land-use techniques.

II. TRADITIONAL STRATEGIES

There is hardly any need to dwell upon the methods of natural resource utilization in underpopulated regions. Everywhere the methods of production are based on extensive cultivation, i.e. temporary land-clearing with long fallow periods for restoring the organic and mineral nutrients removed by the crops. Although there are many variations in this system and various adaptations to local environmental conditions and to the type of cultivation involved, this is the usual system of all tropical environments. The only specifically Sudan features worthy of note are the antiquity of the system and the selectivity in forest clearing. The practice of this system over the centuries has caused a degradation of the climax plant associations, i.e. of the dry forest, resulting in their adaptation to fire and their replacement by various savannas going from the most wooded types to the most open ones. As for selective forest clearing, it is the cause of the usual park landscapes of the savannas and their species composition. All the savannas dominated by karite, African locust bean trees, tamarind trees and locally baobabs and fan palms, are evidence of selective forest clearing techniques which have precise objectives and are part of a planned strategy. Thus karite, for example, has a random distribution which has nothing to do with natural conditions. Its limitation to the West by the River Falémé, its uneven density and occasionally its absence within a suitable environment, result from the needs and the choice of the peoples who have selected it in the naturally occurring vegetation and who have systematically helped it to survive and spread. The truest of paeleo-Sudan civilizations includes both farmers and stockmen. They obtain the fats in their diet from the milk of their animals and ignore the karite. On the contrary, the butter extracted from the karite fruit is used daily by the purely agricultural peoples and by the peoples where livestock is in the minority. The karite savanna is thus the product of an intentional strategy on the part of the people deprived of cattle or of farmers who have not, or at least only to a limited extent, integrated cattle-raising into their activities.

However, the most sophisticated and differentiated strategies for using and managing natural resources are found within the highly populated regions. A fundamental distinction can be made, based on the origin of this population density, as to the levels to which population has risen and to the supporting political structures. Firstly, the paeleo-Sudan peoples, whose organization depended on a lineage-based cohesion and solidarity, could only intensify their production system through progressive and increasingly sophisticated management of their environment. Secondly, the societies possessing hierarchical structures and an efficient political organization have had, and still have, the possibility of meeting the demands of their population increase by expanding their territories or by bringing in or using resources from outside their own lands.

Essentially two cases will be used to analyse the strategies of the first group. These cases are both similar and different as they are situated at two extremes of the Sudan zone and in environments as opposite as coastal swamps and mountains.

The Diola, Balant and Baga peoples are spread out on the section of the coast called the 'Rivières du Sud' (covering the Casamance region, Guinée-Bissau and Guinée-Conakry). These peoples are closely related both by their social system and their techniques of paddyfield rice cultivation which require very careful management of natural conditions. Here, the low plateaux sink under the coastal muds which are interwoven by a dense network of streams, deeply penetrated by estuaries, covered with forests and surrounded by thick mangroves. Access and exploitation of this environment are both difficult; however, it offers a variety of natural resources. There are relatively rich forests where coastal humidity is enough for oil-palms. Soils are varied and fertile, generally deep loose sands and fine alluvium. Rainfall is abundant (at least 1,500 mm) but it has a Sudan distribution (seven months dry season). There is a great range of possible crops, and the streams are well stocked with fish. Tse-tse flies are present in the rain forests, but they can be eliminated by clearing the forest, thus permitting cattle raising, and even more so as the origin of the trypanoresistant N'Dama race of cattle, the Fouta-Djallon, is not far away. The forests, mangrove swamps, streams and off-shore bars surrounded by swamps served as refuges for the peoples who had no political structure but were fervently opposed to any type of dependence and, above all, were concerned with defending their liberty and all the peasant values of paeleo-Sudan societies. They thus survived the Foulani and Manding assaults, enveloped in their resolute hostility towards all outside influences, as faithful to their ancestral animism as to their long exclusive choice of rice cultivation. For a long time, Islam and colonization were unable to broach their resistance, and modern governments often come up against their independence, if not their insubordination. For a long time, their population increase was very slow because of internal strife resulting from the absence of any superior authority in the village, or even in individual neighbourhoods. The increasing numbers of these obstinate people were confined to one area, which is why densities frequently exceed 50 inhabitants/km^2. In the paddyfield areas, for example, of the Diola people of the Lower Casamance region, or the Floup or the Balant peoples of Guinée-Bissau, one cannot help being struck by the fact that the land is always managed in the same way, using identical techniques that have gradually developed with the same strategies. In the range of possible crops, these peasant farmers have decided on rice, which is the basis and the symbol of their civilization. As they are people of the land, although they live on the coast, they do not go out fishing, turn their backs on the ocean and disregard the streams abounding with fish, which today are being exploited by incoming fishermen. Their own catches are limited to fish caught in the paddyfields and the collection of oysters. Therefore, above all, their cultivated land is used for growing rice. Three elevations of paddyfields can be distinguished, running without a break from the edge of the plateaux to the heart of the mangrove swamps. Upriver, generally at the back of the villages, the paddyfields lie on slopes or low plateaux. The permeable soil holds water with difficulty and, under the palm trees, these areas look more like rice fields rather than paddyfields. Yields are low and unreliable in dry years. Lower down, there are the paddyfields of the plains which have more compact sandy-clay soils able to retain water for a longer period. In spite of the absence of any irrigation techniques, these paddyfields are flooded every year, as is shown by the size and the regularity of yields. Finally, downriver, the lowest paddyfields won back from the mangroves, i.e. on salty soils, are veritable polders whose construction merits detailed examination. It is an arduous business

felling the dense stands of mangroves and transforming the salty muds into arable soils. The first task is to surround the felled area which is to become paddyfields by a solid dike higher than the level of the highest tides. The second step consists in desalting the soil. Wide ridges separated by deep ditches are built to this effect through an exhausting amount of work. The winter rains gradually wash out the chlorides which then accumulate in the ditches and are periodically evacuated by sluices in the outer dikes opened at low tide. After many years of this treatment, the ridges are suitable for cultivation. They are deep-ploughed and planted out with rice. Their position downriver means that these paddyfields are abundantly and sometimes excessively supplied with water. However, it is possible to use the streams for flooding the paddyfields if they have been sufficiently diluted with surface run-off. Opening and closing the sluices means that the water-level in the polders can be regulated so that the rice has its roots in water without being vulnerable to rice-eating fish, and that weeds are kept down to a maximum. Treated with such care at the price of considerable effort, these low-lying paddyfields give the highest yields, except during serious droughts when the salt level rises to the upper soil horizons. It is quite disconcerting to realize that such an undertaking of environmental management and transformation is carried out on a family scale, if not of just a few related households. At best, an exchange of labour on the neighbourhood level facilitates the creation or the extension of polders. As soon as the land transformation operations are finished, the area is shared out amongst the adult males of the family group to whom the land belongs. Each plot is then individually owned and cultivated only by the workers of the household, at their own profit. Even though initial constructions justify a collective effort, this is only temporary and immediately afterwards, rice cultivation reverts to being an individual affair, as is characteristic of all productive activities.

The care taken in constructing the paddyfields is completed by the intensive way in which they are managed. A varied range of techniques can be used as needed. First of all, rice varieties are cleverly adapted to the position and the edaphic qualities of the different paddyfields making up the household plot (once African rice, the hardiest and the most resistant to both salt and drought; today, on the best soils, Asiatic rice, immediately adopted as higher yielding). This careful choice of varieties is generally complemented by the seedlings being planted out, the rice having been previously sown in nursery

beds. In addition, the soil is carefully prepared. It is enriched by domestic and animal
manure and sometimes even improved by spreading lime derived from crushed seashells. The
land is regularly and deeply ploughed to bury
the green matter. A native ploughing instrument,
the *kayendo* (a sort of long spade in the form
of an oar) makes the ridges and the furrows.
However, these different techniques are only
possible and indispensable, and therefore carried out, as needed, i.e. in response to population pressure. The paddyfields extend fur-
thest into the mangrove swamps in the most
self-contained villages, where space is limited
and every inch of land disputed. Here the most
intensive techniques are used, with the land
being ploughed more often and the rice planted
out with more care than anywhere else. Each
lineage and even each family chief chooses the
most appropriate strategy for his requirements
and his available labour force. As soon as
there is a reduction in population pressure,
as is frequently the case today when the men
who work in the paddyfields are side-tracked
by other activities, the mangrove swamp invades
the polders and the various intensive techniques
are practised with much less care. Rice cultivation of the Rivières du Sud is declining now
that the internal strife of the Diola and
Balant peoples no longer exists, that cash
crops are becoming more attractive and that
current rural depopulation is more profitable.
The carefully managed land becomes irreversibly
degraded, high yields no longer ensuring, within the context of an open-market economy, a
remuneration worth the effort involved.

Other, less original forms of environmental
utilization complete the list for the coastal
fringe of the Rivières du Sud. These have the
same objectives and the same strategy developed within the context of an age-long, totally sedentary society. For example, each village
is made up of family farms lying under an open
stand of palm trees and fan-palms. These trees
are maintained and used for constructing houses
in this remarkably well-established settlement.
Before being recently devastated to make way
for cash crops, the forests of the plateaux
were for a long time bordered by uniform stands
of palm trees created by repeated, selective
land clearing. Each village palm grove was
strictly shared out, and each tree individually
owned, just as for the paddyfields. The so-
called natural palm grove is thus the product
of intentional land management carried out
without any collective plan or central decision
above the family level, in the same context of
individual freedom as for the people who developed paddyfield rice cultivation.

There probably cannot be an environment more
dissimilar to the Atlantic coast than the Monts
du Mandara (North Cameroun). This is an area
of crystalline horst criss-crossed with volcanic
veins, whose often steep slopes are littered
with a chaos of rocks. Erosion has broken up
the edges into isolated massifs which stand out
sharply in the surrounding plain. The difference
in elevation (altitudes of 800 to 1,200 m,
rising to 1,500 m for the highest peaks) is
sufficient to give a much wetter Sudan climate
(800-1,100 mm rainfall, whereas at the same
latitude the plain receives an average of 100
to 200 mm). Soils are very varied, but the
dominant granitic bedrock gives sands that are
prone to surface erosion. Soils can be differentiated by their texture; however, stones are
everywhere, omnipresent on the slopes and within
the soil profiles. The topographic position
means that very infertile gravelly soils lie
alongside the theoretically more fertile sandy
soils and sandy-clay soils covering the length
of the slopes where rocky outcrops are frequent.
Nevertheless, this unhospitable environment is
one of the most built-up, most efficiently
managed and most profoundly humanized areas of
Black Africa. Population densities often exceed
100 inhabitants/km^2, reaching 200, even 250 and
275 in certain massifs of the mountains to the
North. The most obvious type of land management
undertaken to support such dense populations is
the complete transformation of the slopes into
terraces forming gigantic staircases climbing
right up to the tops of the ridges. The most
impressive and the most carefully maintained
of these terraces correspond to the highest
population density. These systems appear to be
inseparable from high population pressure because
when even an accidental event, or today, emigration, causes it to fall below a certain thresh-
old, these systems start to degrade just as
quickly as the coastal paddyfields are invaded
by the mangrove swamps under the same conditions
as the Rivières du Sud. These terraces run continuously along the hillsides following the
contours. The width and height of the supporting
walls vary with the slope. On the steepest
slopes, the terraces can be as narrow as 40 cm,
but they are generally 4 to 6 m wide. On the
most gentle slopes, there are simple, low walls
made by clearing the fields of stones. The
vertical walls which support and separate the
terraces are usually 1 m high. In the Podokwo
massifs, walls nearly 3 m high have been noted.
These are impressive constructions with a foundation of large rocks upon which stones have
been methodically placed one on top of the other,
taking great care to fit them together. These
walls are maintained every year by a technically

simple operation which requires relatively little effort, but it is always amazing to think of the initial amount of work needed for their construction.

The domestication of the vegetation also indicates how intensively these massifs are managed. All the natural vegetation has disappeared. Cultivation of entire hillslopes eliminates fallow lands and any secondary regrowth. The trees which dot the terraces sometimes form a park with a uniform density of 20 trees/ha. These trees are all useful species, selected and treated as domesticated plants, although most of them occur naturally. This park mainly includes: jujube trees pruned so as to give straight poles to hold up the roofs of houses, and whose fruit is also valued as food; some rubber plants and tamarind trees, also for food; dry zone mahogany trees, whose fruit gives an inedible oil which has many uses, and whose bark is used in the preparation of millet beer; finally acacias, notably *Acacia albida*, whose inverse vegetative cycle makes it so useful for feeding cattle during the dry season, and for fertilizing the soil. With the exception of *A. albida*, these trees would overshadow the crops if left to themselves. Systematic pruning limits this undesirable effect and also provides the wood necessary for everyday use. Thus the utilization of the park is subject to laws that are just as precise as those governing territorial land-use. Managing the hillslopes as terraces not only allows the clearing of the fields of stones, but also regulates the hydrological cycle. Water infiltration is facilitated, thus increasing plant water supplies and considerably diminishing the effects of erosion. Surface run-off is controlled and the whole drainage system benefits, all the way from increasing the number of springs to slowing down floodwaters in the valleys.

As in all situations of this type, this elaborate system of land management supports remarkably intensive cropping systems (Hallaire 1972; Boulet 1975). Each year the whole mountain is covered with fields of millet, and occasionally sorghum as with the Ouldémé people (who have about thirty varieties always carefully graded to edaphic differences), or else sorghum and millet alternated between years as with the Matakam people. The basic cereal-producing system is complemented by sowing crops of beans, okra and sesame between rows, by farming tiny plots of tobacco, small fields of earth pea, and especially ground-nuts if the field spreads onto the pediment. In the absence of any fallow, it is necessary to carefully use the fertilizer available, such as

domestic waste distributed by the rains as the houses lie to the top of slopes; carefully collected animal manure (the human density is such that stock-raising only concerns the 'boeuf de case' (house-hold ox) and a few goats); ashes from kitchen hearths; old roofing straw; in total, rather meagre additions. Taking into account the basic constructions that make it possible to manage the land, it is above all the care and the intensity with which the soil is worked that make it possible to continue farming each individual plot and to ensure the future of this form of agriculture as a whole.

Here again the highly elaborated production techniques and the ways in which the land is managed are accompanied by a social organization made up of groups of autonomous families having stubbornly refused the bondage of any political structure. The mountain peoples form a relatively homogeneous society on both the technical and cultural levels, but they are scattered in a multitude of ethnic groups of very different sizes which only become aware of their common personality when they are confronted with the Moslem peoples of the plain. With only rare exceptions – notably the Matakam people – each mountain corresponds to an ethnic unit. The mountain peasant comes from the massif and not from a village (even the word itself is unknown), and his mountain holds both his fields and his living space. The way in which the houses are laid out is also indicative of this state of extreme social and political dispersal. Even though some thirty meters away from the neighbours (usually their relatives), each individual family shuts itself in an enclosure which looks rather like a small fortress protecting the granaries and straw huts. Hardly any other feature better illustrates the fervent individualism of these mountain peoples. Formerly, a 'chief of the massif' emerged only in times of extreme danger. In principle, he was the head of the oldest lineage, but his authority was only for temporarily co-ordinating defense and was not the authority of a member of a political organization or of a representative of some hierarchical society. This paradox between such social and political dispersal and the magnitude of the work involved in managing the land can be explained by several factors: extremely ancient settlement; the gradual spread of colonization, the active solidarity of populations shut in their mountains as if under siege (even if they are not taking refuge, as is the case for most of these peoples), and above all population pressure. Such a paradox therefore results from the strategy for survival of men attached to their mountain environment since time immemorial (Hallaire 1972).

Another consequence of population density and therefore of the scarcity of land, and also no doubt of the ways in which it is managed, appears in the land-tenure systems. The land has been developed by an age-old effort of these peoples' ancestors. Land is individually owned and highly sought after, and its value depends on the effort made for its development. Here the land has always been free of religious associations or collective management. On the other hand, however, it is subject to varied and incessant transactions, going from the simple loan to outright transfer, or from temporary rental to permanent sale, carried out according to traditional laws which are free from outside influences, for example the use of money (Boutrais 1973). This type of land-use (exceptional in African law) affects the society's whole strategy concerning the mountain environment, and is no doubt a response to population increase inevitably splitting up the lineages and families, trying to mitigate the inequalities in land-tenure that have become intolerable under acute overpopulation.

This situation is evolving. Under the onslaught of enterprising and organized neighbouring populations, colonial power, the national government's desire for unification, and the pull of a money-based economy, there has been, especially since 1960, a dominant tendency towards the 'descente des montagnards', i.e. the people coming down from the mountains. No doubt this is inevitable and, from many points of view, indispensable for a part of the population. However, the attempts at 'planned' colonization of the surrounding plains undertaken during the last fifteen years have yielded inconclusive results indicating that two dangers exist in this respect: firstly, the rapid destruction of these remarkable achievements in land management and an immediate loss of control over the natural ecosystem; secondly, the disappearance of the mountain peoples' cultural identity and the breakdown of the values which they once upheld.

The two preceding examples have been drawn from particularly specific and contrasting natural environments where it was necessary to fully develop paeleo-Sudan production techniques in order to manage the land. Traditionally this took place within the context of family-based strategies aimed at maintaining individual freedom without limiting social or political structures. Environmental control was particularly demanding in these two cases, whereas much more hospitable initial environments exist throughout most of the Sudan region. In these latter cases, the efforts to manage the land are thus essentially reflected in the plant cover. The Bwa example, with exceptionally well-united village communities, gives both a typical and general illustration. The cultivated area of each Bwa village forms a clearing in the dry forest which is surrounded by dense forest serving as hunting areas, land reserves and once as a protection and a refuge against neighbouring villages (Capron 1973). A cross-section from the village to the forest shows that the land has been managed in a definite, universal pattern, with, of course, the necessary adaptations to each village site, notably the soil type and eventual outcrops of laterite. Each village is immediately surrounded by a narrow belt of enclosed plots under the shade of some baobabs or silk cotton trees. These are really gardens, producing tobacco, maize and condiments. The soil is carefully enriched by every scrap of household waste. Beyond these gardens lies a park regularly planted out with *Acacia albida* trees. This is a typical example of land management for permanent cropping where lineage-based institutions and land ownership take on religious and social connotations. The soil is fertilized by the trees, by the cattle that use this area as common grazing land during the dry season, and also by regular manuring. Fallow periods are not necessary: sorghum, millet and maize are grown together and are alternated in rotation with cotton. A third belt appears beyond this zone, running continuously from the *Acacia* parkland towards a less well defined limit with the forest. Some fallow is found here, and the land is dotted with karite and African locust bean trees. Finally, this park also merges into the forest, where the only evidence of man's intervention are large, temporary, but isolated clearings topped with useful trees and surrounded by vast stretches of dry forest. This land-use pattern corresponds to a definite strategy and changes according to differences in population pressure and requirements. It means that the *A. albida* park, which is really man-made, lies alongside a park of karite and African locust bean trees which has been created by simply selecting the trees from the neighbouring forest. When population increases, the *Acacia* park is extended and crosses over into the karite and African locust bean tree park which in turn is pushed out further into the forest. When agriculture was concerned only with subsistence farming, the *Acacia* park provided all the essential crops, and the forest was hardly ever used except for hunting and fruit picking. The increase in the numbers of fields cleared of the natural vegetation and in the karite and African locust bean tree parks which result, is due to a period of political peace accompanied by a rise in population requirements, especially with the addition of cash crops, notably cotton. Although this concentric ring pattern of land-use is the result of human concentration in village communities, this same strategy is frequently used by independent family farms. The different land-use elements are organized in strips instead of rings and form a row of fields placed one after another. The type and the intensity of cropping techniques can be identified by the tree cover composition. The presence of an *A. albida* park, in particular, shows how well stock-raising has been integrated into the cropping system, i.e. by using animal manure for maintaining the fertility of continuously cropped fields. This park therefore makes it possible to practise an agriculture that is both sedentary and intensive, since apart from receiving organic matter through leaf fall at the beginning of the agricultural season, the park is also manured by the cattle which can thus spend the dry season on the cultivated lands around the village. It appears that stock-raising is an essential part of the land-use strategy of the paeleo-Sudan peasant societies, except when unusually high population densities cannot afford the appropriate space (as is seen on the most populated massifs of the Monts du Mandara). This is not the case in places where population density results mainly from a political policy, and the peasant farming techniques and values have been placed in the background by an introduced system of organization.

The traditional strategy of this type of society will be analysed using the Mossi area as an example. Here, a hierarchical power structure has engendered high population density. The indigenous original population and prisoners of war were grouped together in an abnormally dense settlement where there was total disregard for the environment and its natural resources. It is impossible to identify a single Mossi farming system because the Nakomsé political aristocracy, taking no interest in land-use techniques, did not impose a particular system, but respected (or ignored) the various systems that existed before they arrived. For this reason, paeleo-Sudan-type technical practices and landscapes have survived (for example, the *A. albida* parks on the edge of the Birrimic chain of mountains in the western part of the Mossi area: some are still being used, while others form fossil landscapes with no relation to the current methods of land-use). However, over most of the Mossi plateau, man has simply exploited and destroyed the

landscape, just as with a mining economy, and no traces can be found of any kind of environmental control or constructive intervention. The cropping system is based on two types of fields. Firstly, there are the more or less permanent 'champs de case' (household fields) with the family houses, which, grouped together, often represent part of the same lineage and form a village quarter. Secondly, there are the 'champs de brousse' (fields cleared of their natural vegetation) which form a ring around the limits of the first type. However, due to the density of population, the land clearing practices are becoming more sedentary, and fields lie fallow for much shorter periods, to the extent that the two types of fields start to resemble each other. It can just be seen that the second type has a greater variety of weeds, and a higher density of selected plant species, notably karite. Millet and sorghum dominate everywhere. Lack of space and very low yields keep cash crops at a marginal level or eliminate them completely. Within this agricultural system, there is an almost total absence of stock-raising. The Mossi agriculturalists very rarely keep cattle and then in very limited numbers. This situation is probably very ancient, resulting both from the peasants' inability to put aside and save surplus goods, the chiefs' monopolization of the cattle (cattle being one of the most desirable elements for a military and political hierarchy living off tributes and their takings), and finally, too passive an attitude towards soil exhaustion, an attitude developed through the peasants' dependence on the social and political system which had assimilated them. On the other hand, the peasants are very keen on raising smaller animals and keeping poultry, whose produce is easily sold. Since peaceful relations have been established among neighbouring ethnic groups, the Mossi cultivated lands have been enriched by the Foulani herds of cattle which temporarily stay near their villages.

A short time ago, the military power and political influence of the Mossi people allowed them not only to take captives which then became the agricultural labour force, but also to bring in, with or without their consent, some of the harvest of the peoples settled at the borders of the territory directly under their administration. Similarly, it was a tradition that in the dry season, a certain number of Mossi inhabitants left their country in order to hunt, gather fruit and exchange their varied craft goods (unknown to the peasant farming populations) in markets for food. Thus through their organization and the external influence which stemmed from it, the Mossi people were able to use the resources from a very much larger area than that limited by their political frontiers. In order to understand how the dense settlement built up by the Nakomsé peoples lasted such a long time, in spite of infertile soils and the low efficiency of production techniques, it is necessary to consider the Mossi area's highly structured political and social organization. The Nakomsé leaders organized the population and imposed a cultural unity and solidarity which, all through the course of history, allowed the Mossi inhabitants and their chiefs to use the resources from a much larger area than that under their direct administration.

Indeed, the basic factors behind the Mossi spatial dynamism continue to work in the profoundly different situations created by colonization and later by contemporary political organizations. They partially support the high population densities (or make such densities tolerable), by bringing in resources from outside the Mossi territory, including those from other countries.

It has already been noted that the Mossi area has one of the highest emigration rates of the Sudan zone; hundreds of thousands of people have left permanently or temporarily to live elsewhere. Permanent emigration reduces pressure on local resources and leads to a complete break with the region of origin, whilst temporary migrations bring in money and manufactured goods to the families remaining in the villages. The Mossi settlements therefore continue to live off incoming resources. The use of money essentially results from the migrants' sending their earnings in foreign plantations and building sites: yesterday in Ghana, today in the Ivory Coast. At the present time, two simultaneous forms of migration are taking place (Kohler 1971, 1972). The first, in central Upper Volta, concerns the agricultural colonization of the Mossi country's peripheral region, which is underpopulated or uninhabited and which offers new lands for settlement. The second essentially concerns the migration of workers who are temporarily hired as labourers outside the national frontiers. The first type generally involves families who have no intention of returning; the other, mainly young men; there is, however, a whole range of situations between the two. During the last fifteen years, an increasing number of temporary migrants have come back to marry in their villages before leaving to settle as planters in the Ivory Coast forests, where they first stayed as unskilled labourers. The strategy behind these migrations, from the type of people involved to the ways in which

they settle, is directly influenced by the Mossi social system. Three illustrations can be cited. The fact that the elders rule over their brothers and unmarried sons by using their labour force before any other, and that they make it difficult for them to become economically independent, helps to explain which type of person migrates and what direction is taken: young couples wishing to break away and acquire adequate land, often move to new territories; unmarried men wanting to earn money independently move to forest plantations. Similarly, the Mossi people maintain their ancestral means of production. They are very good at clearing the forest, but care little about agricultural land management, hardly give any consideration to the vegetation or the soil, and carry out the most expeditious of cropping techniques at an alarming rate. For example, in the forests which formerly covered the Bwa country, they have made vast clearings dotted with damaged trees next to the parks encircling the native villages. However, soil fertility is not maintained except by occasional short fallow periods. A third aspect of the Mossi cultural heritage is manifested in the strategy behind their emigration and agricultural colonization, which helps to explain the magnitude of the first phenomenon and the effectiveness of the second. The Mossi migrant or colonist is never alone; he always joins up with other Mossi people and enters a group with a familiar social structure. As soon as the Mossi emigrants form a group, a 'chief' appears and recreates a Mossi society around him, whether in the newly-colonized areas, the building sites in the forest, or in the towns where there is a separate Mossi quarter. Blood relations play a decisive rôle in the social structures, the route taken by the emigrants and the designation and the acknowledgement of the chiefs. This natural ability to colonize new areas, reconstitute a familiar and united society and form well-disciplined groups hundreds of kilometers away from their country of origin, is a direct consequence of the traditional Mossi structures and the philosophy that they engendered. Examples are found in every area where the Mossi people have established themselves, from the Samo country in the Sahel, to the pioneer front in the Taï forest in the South-West Ivory Coast. Analysis of Fouta-Djallon emigration or of the Haoussa people's geographical movements would show that, within different biogeographical and sociological contexts, the procedures and the causes behind such long-lasting, efficient organizations are identical, and that they are always accompanied by a comparable indifference towards managing the natural environment.

Finally, it should be emphasized that, far from always seeking to create densely-populated settlements, the main objective of the strategies elaborated by politically structured societies has often been to obtain territorial control through hierarchical organization and military power. Expansionism is thus associated with a well-distributed population, moderate population densities, geographical movements around a close network of flourishing fixed settlements, and clustered villages. The regions that are entirely made up of Manding settlements give typical examples of this type of spatial organization and reaction towards the natural environment. In the Upper Niger or Central Casamance regions, for example, social stratification does not result from successive waves of population movement, but from the society's internal organization. Chiefs and freemen once ruled over a mass of servile labourers and different castes of craftsmen, some of whom are still very active today, since work specialization was compatible with social hierarchy and solidarity. The women were, and often still are, responsible for most of the peasant farming activities, their status making them largely economically dependent. Men carried out, and still carry out, the 'noble' activities, once war and trade, particularly slave-trading, now money-making activities, notably cash cropping. All the activities of the clustered villages are organized collectively. The villages are surrounded by concentric rings of fields and vast stretches of forest used for hunting and shifting cultivation and as rangeland for cattle. However, there is no rational land-tenure; soil fertility is not maintained by a planned strategy; apart from some remaining trees (tamarind, African locust bean tree, fan palms) there is no park; and stock-raising is not systematically integrated into agricultural activities. The Manding society therefore really was, and still is, the prototype of societies where increasing population numbers and needs were basically met by spreading out. This strategy is diametrically opposed to that of paeleo-Sudan peasant cultures where the low level of organization was, and still is, associated with a remarkable aptitude for intensifying production systems.

III. MODERN DECISION-MAKING AND OUTSIDE INTERVENTION

Public authorities have been slow to intervene in the Sudan zone, and the actions they have taken have often been hesitant or indirect. There are three general reasons for this. In the first place, there was the difficulty of intervening in the various peasant cultures, where it was not easy to change elaborate production techniques and complex systems of land management. For a long time, the Sudan peasant populations were considered a potential workforce from which the necessary labourers came to develop neighbouring areas, but no-one thought about developing their own particular environment. Secondly, although there are exceptions, the Sudan area did not offer the vast underpopulated valleys of the Sahel or the lush, uninhabited forests of the equatorial zone, which are suitable for field experimentation of new techniques devised by engineers or speculative planters. The third reason is the small range of crops suitable for international markets. For a long time, crops were limited to ground-nuts and cotton; only recently sugar-cane (and only to a very small extent) has been cultivated. Again, it was only when truly national development policies were elaborated that the public authorities paid attention to the crops supplying the home market. In addition, for a long time, the Sudan zone was ignored by large-scale investment and major development projects.

The first type of intervention based on research and financed by public money involved traditional peasant cultures, and aimed at improving production efficiency and the adoption of new cash crops. Such intervention took place in the villages and in the village farms, introducing methods for increasing production, which, in principle, did not change the existing structures. However, it is obvious that the introduction of new techniques, or even of new crops, will affect the whole mechanism of the production system, modify land allocation, work routines and distribution of labour, share out the profits amongst the members of the family community or different social categories. Thus this sort of intervention has important repercussions which are not only difficult to control, but also difficult to foresee.

A good example of public intervention in 'traditional' peasant cultures is the 'opération arachide-mil' (ground-nut-millet project) undertaken in Senegal from 1965 to 1970. Since the colonial era, Senegal has specialized in producing ground-nuts, which were the main source of income for the peasant populations, the basis of an important sector of industry, and for a long time the only produce suitable for export. Following decolonization and the resulting disappearance of a regime favouring exports to the French market, the national revenue dropped because ground-nut prices were aligned with world exchange rates. As ground-nuts were produced by several hundreds of thousands of peasant farms, any effort at developing production had to be carried out at the level of each individual farm. Indeed, ground-nuts had been gradually incorporated into Senegalese cropping systems under the pressure of a market economy, backed up by the colonial administration. From the beginning of this century, this legume was used in rotation with different varieties of millet, forming the basis of a subsistence agriculture. The sandy soils, the climate over most of Senegal and the tools and techniques of the native population were all suitable for growing ground-nuts, and following the reduction in fallow practices, ground-nuts were adopted in the crop rotations. To promote Senegalese production, the public authorities needed only to conduct some efficient, thorough research, notably on improving cultivars, and to take direct measures to organize commercialization, create the facilities concerned, and fix the prices. Ground-nut production *per se* was, however, ensured only by traditional techniques. Although the rise in population numbers made it possible to double the area of the 'ground-nut basin' in three generations, even increased traditional production was unable to counteract the effects of the sudden drop in prices. Consequently, in 1964, the government of Senegal decided to make an unprecedented effort in intensifying production by disseminating research results and allocating considerable human and financial resources to communicate them to the farmers. This was a national project aimed not only at boosting the income of the poorest peasant farmers, but also that of the State. Decisions concerning the project as well as its execution was the direct responsibility of the government, i.e. of the political power structure. The entire State administration had to support this project concentrated in the ground-nut basin and involving more than half the peasant farms of the country. The project was also important on a national scale, given the amounts of money devoted to it, the rôle of ground-nuts in the country's economy, and its ideological significance, this project being a test of the country's desire to progress and become economically independent.

Several decades of agronomical research had come up with some technical innovations, which, when applied systematically and collectively, made it possible to guarantee a 25 per cent increase in yields for the normal peasant farmer. These innovations were included in a series of 'thèmes techniques' (technical programmes) which the agronomists considered the peasants could pick up easily. These programmes included systematic use of selected varieties, seed disinfection, use of the animal-drawn drill and hoe to sow at the optimum density and facilitate weeding, rationalization of crop rotations, and fertilization using appropriate amounts of chemical products. A system of credit was set up so as to apply these techniques and finance purchases of tools and fertilizer. Thus the whole area was supplied with the necessary equipment for applying the technical programmes. However, in spite of the initial subsidies, the peasants ran heavily into debt. One of the most important aspects of the project was the necessity to popularize research knowledge, giving the peasants both general and technical instruction through a team of educators who were always present in the field. Owing to the size and the quality of this effort, which required so many personnel that a great many foreign assistants were called in to help, this development project should be considered above all as an exceptional investment in the general education of the local population, which aimed firstly at intensifying production, and secondly at improving the level of the farmers' technical knowledge. It was therefore an overall effort to modernize a traditional agricultural system going far beyond simply the production of ground-nuts. This served as justification for financial support, and as a basis for the agronomical programme. The project was resolutely carried out although, after five years, results fell short of initial expectations. However, these results indicate the populations' reactions to modern decision-making, and the extent to which traditional strategies adapt to technical innovations introduced from outside.

With respect to production, the statistics show that the project was unquestionably a failure. As the project progressed, not only did the tonnages of ground-nut sales fail to increase, but they fell to the point where, in 1970, they were about half the maximum figures recorded in the five years before this intervention. The main reason for this decrease was the unforseeable bad weather which prevailed in Senegal throughout the project's duration. Insufficient and poorly distributed rainfall during rainy seasons which either arrived late or ended prematurely caused reduced yields and led the farmers to devote all their efforts to obtaining sufficient food, i.e. concentrating on millet to the detriment of ground-nuts. At the same time, the farmers were discouraged by national economic difficulties, since during the first three years of the project, the purchase price of ground-nuts fell by almost 25 per cent. The decrease in the peasants' income was made even greater by the illicit trading and money-lending which developed as a result of the growing scarcity of money in the countryside, and the weaknesses in the State system of commercialization.

These were the direct causes of the immediate failure of the development of ground-nut production. However, it is also necessary to mention the causes which arise from the design *per se* of this project. Modern decision-making relied too much upon technical innovations, and assumed that the various social, demographic, and land-tenure situations, etc., were not worth considering. Similarly, the value and significance of the traditional cultures and techniques of the peoples concerned were ignored. One of the first consequences of this attitude was that the 'bassin de l'arachide' (ground-nut basin) was treated as a uniform area for the adoption of the technical programmes. Thus the project was planned as if it were possible, for example, to apply the same norms for equipment to small plots of land which were dispersed over regions supporting nearly 100 inhabitants/km^2 with an over-abundant labour force, as well as to vast farms recently cleared of vegetation to support population densities five to ten times smaller, where machinery had to compensate for the chronic lack of workers in relation to the surface area seeded. Nor did modern decision-making pay attention to land-tenure structures, although the peasant would have had a very different reaction to being asked to invest, and therefore to owe money, according to whether he was a chief of a farming community and therefore certain of his right to the land, or to whether he was a temporary, insecure land tenant. The same ignorance existed in relation to traditional strategies for land-use (i.e. also neglecting the differences in population density), although the ground-nut basin contained different 'ethnic regions'. Well-established peasant cultures, which for a long time practised sedentary and even intensive agriculture, existed alongside recently occupied areas of extensive agriculture, sometimes still at the pioneer stage. It was quite unrealistic to expect that the same technical innovations applied in such different contexts could be adopted to the same extent and have identical results. This ignorance lead decision-makers to draw up *petitio principii* that the increase in production should exclusively stem from the increase in yields. However, all experience of peasant farming shows that an increase in intensification is hardly ever accompanied by an equivalent rise in productivity. It is not that the farmers are ignorant of the fact that,

whenever land is available, it is more profitable to increase the cultivated surface area (and thus use animal-drawn machinery), than to systematically increase yields with more labour and a costly investment in fertilizers. More generally, the lack of knowledge about the situations existing in Senegal could only lead to overestimating the project's results, since, in reality, the potential increases in production differed greatly from region to region.

An examination of the results of a modern type of decision-making and of the investments concerned should not be limited to immediate economic success or failure. In reality, the effort made in teaching the technical programmes had a considerable impact on the rural populations. Firstly, it brought out the peasants' desire to progress and their ability to pick up new methods, as shown by their investment and the speed with which they became familiar with the proposed techniques. Sowing in rows and using an animal-drawn hoe for weeding were adopted all over the 'ground-nut basin' within three or four years. This educative effort also showed that the farmers had a critical, selective attitude towards the innovations, which were in fact being put to the test by the users. Thus, for example, the use of chemical fertilizers was quickly limited for clearly justified agronomical or economical reasons. In the same way, the combination of insufficient rainfall and unfavourable economic difficulties allowed the peasants to demonstrate their sense of responsibility and freedom of judgment by using the techniques originally intended to increase ground-nut productivity for improving cereal production. The cultivation of millet was thus improved through a project designed for cash crops, to the extent that the rural population's food supplies, one of the peasants' major concerns, did not deteriorate in comparison with the sudden drop in their incomes. One of the project's results was therefore to reduce the impact of drought on subsistence crops, with even a considerable revival of these crops.

The project had generally unpredicted repercussions on cropping systems. Thus the use of the animal-drawn drill and hoe allowed the peasant farmers to extend the area under active cultivation, with different consequences in different regions. For example, in the Sérèr country, where high population pressure had prevailed for a long time, the spread of agricultural tools speeded up the disappearance of the three-year millet-ground-nut-grazed fallow rotation, and the entire area was put under cultivation, a practice which puts a strain on soil fertility. In the underpopulated areas of Terres Neuves, the introduction of animal-drawn agricultural equipment did nothing to intensify cropping techniques. However, it did allow the most enterprising and best equipped chiefs of the farming communities to extend forest clearing, which was really part of a deliberate strategy of territorial control. This meant that the project also had important social effects. The so-called 'paysans de pointe' (top peasants) were to be found everywhere. They made use of their former land possessions, the abundant labour-force of their families or the facility with which they could obtain credit owing to their social position. They were regarded as leaders alongside the other chiefs of farming communities, and sometimes became real entrepreneurs. The spread of agricultural equipment simultaneously affected the work routine and the employment situation. Almost everywhere, mechanization of the most labour-consuming tasks (particularly weeding) resulted in a regression of collective mutual aid, underemployment in overpopulated areas, and finally in a decline in the rôle of seasonal workers in areas where there was once an insufficient labour-force. In the same way, modernization of techniques either created or accentuated differences between individual farms in the village communities. Thus, on the social level, the lessons on how to use the equipment for agricultural progress were an added factor giving rise to hierarchism and social inequalities.

Finally, in spite of the fact that the technical programmes were uniformly applied, they accentuated regional disparities. Overcrowding in the ancient cultivated lands of the West ground-nut basin became more apparent than ever, whereas the superiority in size and farm income of the Terres Neuves of Saloum was emphasized. In the regions where farms were large enough to adopt animal-drawn techniques, the most obvious increase in income did not stem from these new methods, but rather from the sale of working animals. The farmers quickly realized the advantage of periodically renewing their animals, which, when well-cared for, provided excellent meat. This indirect result of a project for ground-nut production, particularly apparent in Saloum, is yet another example of how differently peasant cultures can react to such a project, and the failure of decision-making bodies to account for their ability to take initiatives.

The second example of intervention by government decision with public financing concerns the traditional cultivated lands in the Sénoufo country in the North Ivory Coast. One of the differences with the preceding project is that here a food crop - rice - is a source of income

for the farming population. A rural area with high population density, almost one hundred inhabitants/km^2, is found around Korhogo, on the plateau limited by the Bandama River valley, itself uninhabited until now because of onchocerciasis. For a long time, this was a marginal area compared to the rest of the Ivory Coast's economy. A branch of the Sénoufo people had long taken refuge there, isolated next to the frontier with Upper Volta and unable to participate in the plantation-based economy in the forest zone, except by sending some labourers. Until recently, they exclusively practised intensive, mixed subsistence cropping, based essentially on yams and sorghum, complemented by maize, rain-fed rice, millet, beans and groundnuts. During the last thirty years, the Sénoufo people have been able to deal with their population explosion through continuously improving crop associations and the paddyfields built on the lowlands which cut the plateau. However, these measures did not stop them from becoming poorer and poorer, until around 1960, their income was about five times less than that of the planters in the forest zone. The State decided to intervene and redress these differences by assigning to a public company the development of irrigated rice cultivation, the national market being a profitable, largely unchallenged opening for rice sales. This project was based on the existence of small, relatively unexploited valleys, many of which had perennial ponds, in an area of intensive cropping in the uplands. There was also an overabundance of labourers, who were reputed for the quality of their agricultural traditions (Coulibaly 1974). The project had considerable financial backing, the money being used not only to construct the necessary infrastructure, but also to set up an elaborate programme generally educating the population, which was efficiently carried out by experts from China.

Irrigated rice cultivation was implanted using a pragmatic, progressive strategy. The first step was to take the flooded paddyfields that the peasants had constructed on the lowlands and in the small valleys of the densely populated zone, and transform them into irrigated paddyfields. Using simple techniques, the paddyfields were first of all levelled, then divided into plots separated by dikes, supplied with water by making channels coming off the stream-line, and drained by canalizing the central thalweg. Yields were higher and more regular. The peasants enthusiastically participated in this concrete effort to improve the land. The project did more than affect rice cultivation in the rainy season, for, in the dry season, it was possible to make a second harvest in the first paddyfields alongside the perennial ponds, the area irrigated being limited, however, by the flow of the perennial springs. This second harvest was a change in the usual inactivity of the dry season, and very quickly it became the peasant farmers' major objective. This practice could not be extended because of lack of water, and could only be carried out on 15 per cent of the area under paddyfields during the rainy season. This explains the second step in the development of the project, begun about 1970. Small earth dams were constructed upriver of the first paddyfields, which, in the dry season, held back the water necessary for a second harvest. This project's success and the fact that the farmers were so keen to benefit from this type of development, lead to a third stage, which is still being carried out. Large dams are being constructed, serving much larger areas of about one thousand hectares. These are at the edge of the densely populated zone, in the underpopulated valleys which served as the outer boundaries of this region. Thus began a policy for relieving the most populated zone by spreading the population out into the peripheral areas, and by gradually gaining new lands added on to the first stages of the project, which, it will be remembered, only aimed at intensifying cultivation in the traditional Sénoufo lands.

While the various developments were being constructed, a group of educators taught the techniques necessary for using them efficiently: maintenance of canals and dikes, sowing in nursery beds, planting out in rows, repeated weeding, use of fertilizers, regulating the waterlevel in the paddyfields, etc. These were quickly picked up by the Sénoufo farmers, whose hard-working nature (and especially their skill at ploughing) complemented the innovations derived from methods used in the Far East. The results can be seen first of all in the statistics for production. Yields usually reach 4 t/ha for each harvest, i.e. 8 t/ha and sometimes even more, whereas a short time ago, the flooded paddyfields only yielded one to two tons. The project has also increased the rural population's income, as shown by the rise in consumption of factory goods, the activity of the markets, increased movements, the development of farm equipment, etc. Lastly, the project's success is apparent in the landscape itself, particularly in the dry season, when, flying over the Sénoufo plateau, one can pick out the green paddyfields stretching along the small valleys. However, this success owes a great deal to the fact that the general economic situation favoured this project, as the

Ivory Coast market and especially the towns on the coast were able to absorb the increasing quantities of rice. In addition, rice prices tended to rise because of a national policy to support and develop the cultivation of major food crops. The public authorities did not limit their interest in the renovation of the Sénoufo country to developing rice cultivation. Another type of development concerned the rain-fed cultivated lands of the densely-populated zone. First of all, there was an effort to spread the use of animal-drawn agricultural equipment so as to hasten ploughing of the plateau fields, and at the same time, free the labourers necessary for the irrigated paddyfields. Thus rain-fed cultivation and cultivation of the lowlands on the plateau would not clash so much in the agricultural timetable at the beginning of the rainy season. Secondly, the public authorities began reafforestation programmes to control erosion on the hillslopes in a region completely cleared of vegetation. Until now, these innovations have been less convincing than rice cultivation. On the one hand, they are much slower in showing any results, and on the other hand, reafforestation did not involve the village economy. It is understandable that the peasants are not very interested in an innovation that is debatable in an overpopulated region. Finally, two projects promoting cash crops were set up next to the densely populated Sénoufo zone because of the need to overcome regional disparities and to develop the backward economy of a Sudan region which derived its riches from a forested zone. One of these projects involves cotton, and is situated to the West and South of the densely populated zone where the low number of inhabitants meant that cotton could be introduced in the cycle of food crops. The other concerns sugar cane, which is cultivated using irrigation within an agro-industrial complex of 6,000 ha near to Ferkessédougou, and supplied with water from a dam on the Bandama River. These projects should help to relieve population pressure around Korhogo through emigration both to the sugar cane complex and to the still sparsely populated areas suitable for cotton cultivation. It is still too early to appreciate the results of these interventions, especially since the successful project intensifying rice cultivation has, at least temporarily, absorbed the available labour-force and satisfied the immediate aspirations of the farmers in the densely populated zone around Korhogo. Nevertheless, the temporary results of projects undertaken by public authorities during the past twelve years indicate that the Sénoufo country is no longer a marginal area of the Ivory Coast. The changes that have taken place, and especially the success of irrigated rice cultivation, make it possible to predict a rapid improvement in the rural population's living conditions. The rural population is at last able to participate in inter-regional exchanges, as it specializes in supplying the plantations and the towns. This has been possible within the context of a strategy for development which concerned the entire national territory.

Projects to relieve areas of high population density and the simultaneous organization of colonization in peripheral areas, are another form of intervention by public authorities. Areas which have been particularly concerned by this type of project are the overpopulated mountain ranges, where for a long time, paeleo-Sudan peoples have defied government authority and kept to the fringe of the market economy. Some of these projects date back to the beginning of the colonist era, as is the case in Togo, in the Kabré massif. Others are much more recent, and have only become really important since independence, as in North Cameroun, which shall be taken as an example. These projects can be very schematic when they aim at both relieving population pressure in the mountains and colonizing the surrounding plains. They cumulate difficulties because, in addition to the technical complications of intervening in traditional peasant farming cultures, there are also problems arising from the fact that the colonists are strangers, that they must settle in a new environment and become integrated with different societies. It was seen that the North Monts du Mandara has a mountain civilization which is remarkable not only in supporting exceptionally high population densities, but also for the techniques of land management which characterize the landscape. It is even more surprising that these massifs are overpopulated, as they dominate plains with a much sparser population. Consequently, as early as the colonial era, the 'descente des montagnards' (movement of people down from the mountains) became the main concern of a government which wanted at the same time to control these elusive people, tax them, and confront the most important effects of overpopulation on the land (Boutrais 1973). These hopes were doubly motivated by independence. For political reasons the government wished, on the one hand, to integrate these mountain people in the national community, and, on the other, to have them participate in the development of the cash crops of North Cameroun, i.e. ground-nuts and especially cotton. It was during the Second World War that the colonial government tried to make the mountain peoples adopt ground-nut

cultivation. Seed was distributed, fields were watched over, harvests were organized and the people were obliged to pay their taxes with money and not in kind. This forceful intervention finally resulted in the cultivation of small intra-montane basins, and more especially in spreading cultivation onto the sandy foothills of the massifs. It therefore meant that the mountain people could widen their range of crops without encroaching the domain of cereal crops, and increase their cultivated territory without leaving their traditional habitat. After independence, the public authorities were even more determined in their interventions. A series of interventions tended to force the mountain people to abandon their traditional lands, whilst the plain became the site for a project systematically developing cotton cultivation. A great effort was made to teach all the techniques for growing cotton, going from setting up the fields (each peasant farmer having to cultivate at least half a hectare), to commercializing the harvest. Seed distribution, use of animal-drawn equipment, adoption of chemical fertilizer, treatments for controlling plant health were all undertaken by the Compagnie française des textiles (CFDT) (Textile Company of France). The people living in the plains, notably the Mandara and Foulbé peoples, were the first and the most eager to cultivate cotton. However, cotton competed with the subsistence crops, firstly by taking up the sandy-clay soils suitable for millet cultivation, and secondly, by clashing with cereal crops in the agricultural timetable. The farmers of the plain resolved this problem in two ways: they hired labourers coming from the mountains, and cleared the vegetation covering the thin deposits of black clay, previously uncultivated. These areas were used for growing 'mouskouari' (grain sorghum), a transplanted millet whose cycle lags behind that of the rainy season crops, notably cotton. Within a few years, the people of the plain took possession of all the land suitable for growing grain sorghum, mostly due to the work of the mountain people, who became seasonal labourers. In spite of all this, the problems of the mountain areas remained unsolved because the success of cotton provided an economic basis for the ancient conflict between the Islamic people of the plain and the 'pagans' of the mountains.

While the CFDT was carrying out its project, the government increased its interventions encouraging the mountain people to settle in the plain. Two types of measures were taken, which were supposed to be complementary. The first used the State's authority to make the people leave the mountains. The others made arrangements for receiving the mountain people in the plain. These measures were neither carried out on the same scale nor co-ordinated in terms of timing. It was thus that in 1963, a government decision obliged several tens of thousands of people to leave the mountain areas and to settle in the surrounding foothills or in the plain. However, as soon as government pressure slackened, most of these people returned to the mountains, having found that the plain offered neither a way of life nor an economy tempting enough to induce them to stay. Indeed, the Mandara and Foulbé peoples agreed to receive them as labourers and at most rent them some land, but did not want them to settle as rivals. As a result, the government tried to make arrangements for receiving these people. With financial help from the Fonds d'assistance et de coopération (Assistance and Co-operation Fund) and then the Fonds européen de développement (European Development Fund), several areas covering a total of some 20,000 ha were set aside for the colonists from the mountains. These areas were designed according to a theoretical model, with a geometrical lay-out, a grid network of roads, houses dispersed over the blocks of cultivated land and systematic crop rotations, in short, with a rigid, uniform agricultural system which was as inadapted to soil variety as to the individualism of the mountain people. In addition, because they did not dispose of animal-drawn agricultural equipment, or the means to grow 'mouskouari' (grain sorghum), most of the colonists did not manage to make a better living than they had with producing ground-nuts, tobacco and craft goods in their traditional lands. Finally, the considerable amount of money invested in establishing these reserved areas was not followed up by money necessary not only for their maintenance but also for organizing and training the colonists, in spite of the fact that their conduct was supposed to be dictated to them. Although there were some local or individual successes, fluctuating population numbers and shabby housing indicate that the establishment of these colonist reserves offered neither a solution to the problems of the mountain people, nor viable focal points for development which would influence the whole plain area.

Of all the initiatives taken in the last twenty years, only cotton cultivation has been an irrefutable success. This project was undertaken by a specialized company which controlled all the cotton-producing activities and ensured cotton commercialization. It found support in a government which was determined to promote cotton cultivation and use it as a tool for regional growth. However, although this project is positive, economically-speaking, it has done more to reinforce the privileged position of the people of the plain, than to improve the prospects of the mountain people. Consideration of the mountain people was mainly expressed in authoritarian decisions whose outcome would sometimes amount to condemning them completely. However, the reason for these failures lies not only in the methods, but also in the general aims of these projects. Those who planned the government-directed colonization of the plain put all their efforts in elaborating production systems and in applying techniques, whereas the mountain people needed to feel sure of their freedom and security, and to be organized into close-knit communities, before settling down in the plain. Confirmation of their rights to the land, recognition of their cultural independence, and the assurance that their interests would be defended against other possible forms of farming activity would have done more to encourage depopulation of the mountain areas than the most sophisticated agronomical projects. The unprompted emigration towards the foothills already shows very different results from those foreseen in the official project. However, for the mountain people themselves, this emigration amounts to a simple extension of their intensively cultivated lands. This attitude shows that people leave the mountain areas in order to ensure their food supplies. It also shows that the plains North of the River Bénoué are no longer new territories free from any land-tenure control, and thus ideal for real colonization. No doubt this is also a sign that the inevitable high population densities of the plain are largely able to rely on the mountain civilizations. But the national decision-makers need yet to be convinced that a strategy other than that based on cotton cultivation should be employed.

IV. CONCLUSIONS

The decisions of modern political authorities have rarely been concerned with, or capable of, using traditional strategies to their advantage, or exploiting traditional techniques and the knowledge of the environment on which they are based. Such decisions, taken in offices in capital cities, designed to achieve mainly short-term economic results, too often mistaking an increase in exports with real development, are based essentially on the modernization of production techniques for an extremely limited range of cash crops. Interventions by the public authorities have had important repercussions even when they have been unsuccessful. Results have been sometimes unexpected but always instructive, and many lessons can be learnt from the way in which the people concerned have interpreted these interventions. The most important lesson is that Sudan peasant cultures need above all to ensure their food security, and that no amount of external pressure can change this essential preoccupation. The second lesson is that any progress made with agricultural equipment will engender a regression in collective work and a decline in the solidarity of the community. Similarly, technical innovations give rise to social differences and economic inequalities within family and village communities. Another conclusion that can be drawn from the examples which have been described is that the Sudan peasant farmers are very quick to learn. Far from being entrenched in their traditional methods, they master the proposed techniques surprisingly quickly, that is, if they are financially feasible. There again, these new techniques must be really profitable, not necessarily increasing the yields, but rather the amount of money received for the work invested. This means that the intensive cropping techniques used in traditional survival strategies will be sustained only if they are deployed for crops with a much larger market. This also means that when an innovation is rejected, it is not because of the peasant farmers' inability to adopt it, but because it is not considered worthwhile, taking into account their means of production.

Another lesson to remember is that contemporary changes in Sudan societies no longer involve communities but individual people. Traditional strategies used to affect an entire ethnic group, or make the communities react as a united whole. However, modern decisions have more and more the tendency to initiate individual reactions, to facilitate personal promotion, or to interest a single category of the society, e.g. chiefs of farming communities, young people, or women.

Nevertheless, the reactions of a population to modern decisions still depends a great deal on the past structures, for example, the skill or incompetence at territorial control, the ability to organize migration or the inability to come out of isolation, etc. These differences are rarely considered in the decisions taken by public authorities, although acceptance or rejection of these decisions is clearly increasingly related to land-tenure. In addition, in many areas, rational land management requires that the inequalities in ability to expand and colonize should be rectified by State decree and appropriate laws.

Finally, it must be stressed that development cannot take place in a vacuum, and that, to achieve progress in the Sudan zone, the relationships with neighbouring zones must be taken into account. In this respect, a variety of possible actions can be taken by modern public authorities. These interventions should not impose on the farmers predictions and techniques derived from restrictive models. Instead, the farmers should be helped to organize themselves, through the provision of appropriate financial support for initiatives they may take, of available markets and of profitable prices. In other words, there must be viable economic incentives to encourage and increase the Sudan peasants' efforts to adopt new equipment and colonize new areas.

BIBLIOGRAPHY

BOULET, J. 1975. *Magoumaz, pays mafa, Nord-Cameroun.* Atlas des structures agraires au sud du Sahara, 11. Mouton, Paris.

BOUTRAIS, J. 1973. *La colonisation des plaines par les montagnards au nord du Cameroun (Monts Mandara).* Travaux et Documents. ORSTOM, Paris.

CAPRON, J. 1973. *Communautés villageoises bwa (Mali – Haute-Volta).* Mémoires de l'Institut d'ethnologie. Musée de l'Homme, Paris.

COULIBALY, S. 1974. Un exemple de développement volontariste dans la région de Korhogo (Côte d'Ivoire). *Bull. Association des géographes français*, mars/avril 1974, p. 117-131.

HALLAIRE, A. 1972. *Hodogway (Cameroun-Nord).* Atlas des structures agraires au sud du Sahara, 6. Mouton, Paris.

KOHLER, J.M. 1971. *Activités agricoles et changements sociaux dans l'Ouest-Mossi (Haute-Volta).* Mémoires N° 46. ORSTOM, Paris.

KOHLER, J.M. 1972. *Les migrations des Mossi de l'Ouest.* Travaux et Documents. ORSTOM, Paris.

REMY, G. 1968. Les migrations de travail dans la région de Nobéré. *Cahiers ORSTOM, série Sciences humaines*, 4, p. 77-91.

RICHARD-MOLARD, J. 1944. Essai sur la vie paysanne au Fouta-Djalon : le cadre physique, l'économie rurale, l'habitat. *Revue de Géographie alpine*, 32, N° 2, p. 135-239.

SAVONNET, G. 1970. *Pina (Haute-Volta).* Atlas des structures agraires au sud du Sahara, 4, Mouton, Paris.

Traditional strategies, modern decision-making and management of natural resources in forest and preforest zones of Africa

G. Sautter and A. Mondjannagni

I. INTRODUCTION

From the point of view of natural resources and their management, the area under consideration can be best defined according to vegetation and types of crops rather than climatic criteria. This area is covered by an equatorial-type, dense, moist forest bordered by mixed savanna and forest formations. There is a whole range of forest formations, going from the evergreen or rain forest to the deciduous forest. However, in West Africa, the series usually stops after the semi-deciduous forest, which gives way to moist or Guinea savannas (also called preforest or periforest savannas). In general, the area can be characterized as a 'forest-savanna mosaic'. It is impossible to define the limits of the forest and its fringes according to rainfall. Certain weather stations in Lower Togo with less than 800 mm rainfall/year lie within the Guinea zone, whereas others, receiving 1,400-1,500 mm/yr, such as in the North of the Ivory Coast, lie outside this zone.

On large-scale maps, the Guinea zone forms a band more or less parallel to the coast of the Gulf of Guinea. Its Northern limit starts from the Senegalese Casamance region and runs in a fairly straight line, gradually decreasing in latitude towards the East, where it lies only a few degrees North of the Equator in the Eastern part of the Central African Empire.

This forest-periforest savanna complex reaches its maximum span in latitude where the Gulf of Guinea turns towards the South. There is a major break at the level of Lower Togo and Lower Benin which divides it into two, the Libero-eburnean block to the West, and the Nigero-congolese block to the East. Each of these blocks has a characteristic narrow area: the first is at the level of the Ivory Coast (the V of the Baoulé savannas); the second, along the chain of mountains forming the frontier between Nigeria and Cameroun. Much further East, there is another, less pronounced narrow area which more or less coincides with the axis of the Congo and Sangha Rivers. This neck of land, some hundreds of kilometers wide, divides the Atlantic forests to the West from the forests of the Congolese basin to the East. In the intervals between these narrow areas, the forest sometimes overlaps into the mixed zone, or else forms some islands fairly far from the forest limits. The most characteristic example is the Togo plateau North of the mouth of the Volta River. Its Eastern and Western slopes are covered with forests, although it lies far from the general forest limit in this geographical area. The delimitation is even more irregular in central Africa, South of the Equator.

II. TRADITIONAL STRATEGIES

A SOCIETY'S FLEXIBLE STRATEGY FOR USING NATU-
RAL RESOURCES: THE NGBAKA PEOPLE OF THE LOBAYE
VALLEY (CENTRAL AFRICAN EMPIRE)

The Ngbaka people are one of the many peoples living in the Southern forest area of the Central African Empire, South West of Bangui, not far from the Congo border. They live in an area of about 8,000 km^2 and have a relatively low population level and density. There are fourteen administrative 'terres' (lands), of which five have an entirely Ngbaka population. The forest is of the type Aubréville (1948) describes as 'faiblement décidu', i.e. having a small proportion of deciduous trees. The region is fairly flat and criss-crossed by a

Unesco, 1978. *Management of natural resources in Africa: traditional strategies and modern decision-making.* (MAB Technical Notes 9).

dense network of rivers which, in the wettest season, overflow and form marshes.

The first groups of Ngbaka people coming from the East settled in this area at the end of the 18th and at the beginning of the 19th centuries (Thomas 1973). A great many local resources other than soil and water resources were used for food and handicrafts, notably basketwork. Gathering, hunting and fishing were all important. A variety of fruits, the leaves of numerous plants and various insects were gathered. Fields were established each year on swiddens cleared using arduous slash and burn techniques. Even today, plantain bananas hold first place in the list of crops and in the local diet, followed by taro and yams. There were a great many varieties of these three plants. Also cultivated were marrows, gourds, sugar-cane, taros (*Xanthosoma* spp.), sweet potatoes, manioc, maize, tobacco, various sorts of vegetables, green leaves and herbs, sesame and ground-nuts. Most of these plants were 'generally grown together in the same area amongst the stumps and the felled tree trunks. With rare exceptions, these plants received no special treatment during their growth, which meant that the plantations looked rather wild and unkempt' (Sévy 1972). Banana tree plantation was carefully staggered and the main harvest was spread out over time. The banana trees resprouted and, sometime afterwards, depending on the variety, also produced fruit. When food was very scarce, a real harvest took place in the fields re-invaded by the forest. A generalized agro-ecosystem was thus developed, which came very close to the natural structural and reproductive conditions of the forest itself.

Because natural resources were dispersed over this area, the Ngbaka people had to adopt a strategy of spreading out over their territory. Under the uncontested authority of the chiefs, each family group of 10 to 60 people settled away from the other groups. These small family communities, scattered over the territory of the lineage, were fervently independent and highly valued their freedom, which was both the cause and effect of their isolation. As the population numbers of each lineage grew, internal pressure caused the lineage to break up, and each new element settled in the surrounding unappropriated lands, or in the lands lying between other groups or other peoples. There was no lack of land to be cultivated. Today, although food crops are more developed than before, they use up only 1/270th of the available land. Theoretically, this means that the fields, after being effectively used for a maximum of three or four

years, lie fallow for 270 years (Thomas 1973). The fields were never far from the houses, at most 2 km. However, this 'small forest' belonging to the family was surrounded by an infinitely larger 'big forest' where collective rights were sometimes practised over great distances. This vast area served as a reserve for gathering, hunting and fishing. These activities provided an irregular source of food, which limited population densities and was at the origin of the strategy of spreading out. The Ngbaka were 'a people whose way of life was founded on obligatory migration' (Sévy 1972).

From the middle of the 19th century, this equilibrium between population and resources was disrupted through the continual influx of new groups, particularly in relation to the slave raids being carried out further East. Difficulties in co-existence began to arise once the available land was saturated with people. 'When the French took possession of the Lobaye valley, practically the entire Ngbaka population was confined to an area it could no longer leave, surrounded by equally aggressive ethnic groups' (Sévy 1972). It became more and more difficult to find the most appreciated and rarest of resources (e.g. big game), and land became a highly desirable possession. In 1957, 10 collective hunts using nets, each lasting a whole day, yielded a maximum of 10 duikers to be shared amongst 350 people. According to the groups who participated, one of the best hunts brought in between 180 and less than 100 g of meat per person (Sévy 1972). The big hunts of today are preceded by a meaningful rite carried out by the personage who mediates with all things supernatural. This rite consists in 'mourning the hunt', and expressing the 'regret for the past, happy days when game was abundant' (Sévy 1972).

The ancient lineage, made up of five to eight 'families' used to live within the same territory as long as it was of a manageable size. In addition to regulating the reproductive level of these families, the essential functions of the lineage concerned their relationships with their environment, either for improving resource management, or for maintaining the group in harmony with nature through appeasing and purifying rites. In turn, relationships between lineages were of a much higher order, described by some authors as 'unities of population', or 'constellations of alliances'. The purpose of these alliances was to make the area safe through armed defense and the exchange of women. They had both sociological and territorial connotations, as is true for a great many other forest peoples, and they are at the

origin of the 'terres' (lands) of the colonial
administration. The constellations not only
divided the area into larger geographical
units, but also replaced a direct strategy of
natural resources utilization by an indirect
one, which worked through distance and social
relationships.

Although the Ngbaka people are confined to
their present ethnic and geographical area,
they have nevertheless managed to preserve a
fairly mobile existence. The mobility of the
villages, as of the former family huts, has
been defined as 'short range nomadism' (Sévy
1972), which takes place in response to 'an
intimate mixture of practical and supernatural
motives'. The land is cultivated for no longer
than three or four years. Once each year, new
clearings are made in the forest. The Ngbaka
practices clearly differ from those of certain
other peoples of the forests of the Central
African Empire. For example, the Mbwaka people
extend cropping over five to seven years.
After only a few years of fallow, the land is
again cultivated, but for a shorter period,
in the end exhausting soil fertility (Mouton
1954). Forest regeneration is slow and difficult, a situation quite unlike that based
on the Ngbaka practices, which hardly reduce
soil fertility. There are thus two strategies
for forest soils. The first, as practised by
the Bantou people of the Congolese forest,
consists in clearing new fields in the forest
every year. The second tries to reap the benefits of the initial efforts as long as possible,
but at the price of quickly diminishing yields.

The particular feature of the movements of
the Ngbaka people is that they take place over
a large area. Every year there are expeditions
for collective fishing, hunting in large numbers, and collecting caterpillars. Collective
fishing takes place in May. It takes on exodus
proportions; the village is practically des-
erted and all activities move out to a camp
in the middle of the forest. The women carry
out all the essential tasks, being responsible
for damming the chosen river, and then poison-
ing the waters stretch by stretch. The big
hunts take place in June and are much more
mobile. The participants stay away from their
villages for a period that was once as long as
a month at a time, at a distance of at least
thirty kilometers. Lastly, caterpillars are
collected, and the time spent in the forest
can be as long as 7 to 8 weeks. Unlike the
first two activities, a large part of the
'catch' is set aside, grilled, and brought
back to the village. These activities are
seasonal, taking place in the rainy season,
which is broken by a short dry season. There

is therefore a semi-nomadic period of several
months and a sedentary period devoted to growing crops. The yearly timetable is divided
between these two activities, coinciding with
the pattern of land-use mentioned above. Management of natural resources requires the practice
of one or another type of land-use, which in
turn governs the yearly timetable of activities.

A few details of this dualistic pattern
should, however, be explained. Other pursuits
link these two sets of productive activities.
Gathering activities include the collection of
bananas on the abandoned banana plantations,
and, in times of scarcity, of wild yams during
the agricultural season. Another intermediate
activity is the exploitation of oil-palms.
They are used for making wine, and oil is extracted using presses of native design. Whole
families devote themselves to these tasks. This
activity is a non-negligible source of income
in the current money-based economy. Oil-palms
are a side product of agricultural practices
(they reproduce on fallow land). In this region,
they are individually owned, being 'very carefully treated by their owners', which means
that oil-palm exploitation 'goes beyond a simple
gathering activity' (Sévy 1972). In addition
to the collection of palm fruits, there are
other individual forms of gathering, fishing
and hunting, most of which are carried out in
the dry season, fairly close to the village.

With its particular attitude towards natural
resources, the Ngbaka system, as it functioned
after the last war, is interesting in that it
falls half-way between a pure hunting and
gathering system (that of the Pygmies, their
cousins), and an agricultural system which
hardly pays any attention to the resources of
the forest proper. Many other groups of people
have similar life styles. For example, according
to the results of a CEMUBAC investigation, the
Zandé forest people spend 12 per cent of their
time in gathering activities (in the broadest
sense), as opposed to 24 per cent of agriculture.
This ratio is even more significant in that,
at the time of the investigation, the villagers
were still under the pressure of government
authorities encouraging cash crops (Huysecom-
Wolter 1972).

Just after 1930, the colonial authorities
pursued a completely irrational strategy, mal-
treating and restricting the activities of the
Ngbaka people. On the one hand, the colonist
authorities demanded that the Ngbaka increase
their hunting activities, and they were encouraged to hunt for, and then sell, ivory. Very
quickly they were forced into participating
in the frenzied harvest of latex from rubber
trees, to the point where they occasionally

had to neglect their subsistence food crops. In addition, commercial companies decided to buy up palm oil from the local, native presses. However, while the government was obliging the local population to make more expeditions in the forest, it stubbornly pursued a policy for regrouping this population, concentrating the people in villages transferred next to the roads traced out in the 1920s. This was done in order to have a tighter control over the population and to settle them away from the rubber and oil-palm plantations.

The forest areas of the present Central African Empire were one of the many underpopulated regions of French-speaking Africa where this policy of concentrating the rural population was carried out. In the Ngbaka region, the local people assembled in the houses beside the roads, and spontaneously used the new axes for transport. On the other hand, however, the Ngbaka people had a tendency to refuse the principle of grouped villages. When government pressure slackened, almost everywhere the people began to spread out again, this time in hamlets dotted in straight lines along the roads. Today, the regrouping policy has again become very important in Africa, this time it aims no longer at facilitating administrative and medical control, but at making the groups large enough so that they can be provided with certain materials. In this new form, the regrouping policy was first applied in Gabon in about 1950 (Pauvert and Balandier 1952; Sautter 1966). At the beginning of the 1960s, the Bamiléké plateau became another trial area for this policy in a completely different political context. Finally, in the last few years, the East and South-East African countries have been using this policy in the woodland regions; examples can be cited of 'villagization' in Tanzania, and especially in Mozambique, where the regrouping was highly ideological. The Ngbaka example should serve as a warning. Indeed, there is a serious risk involved in any policy which aims at concentrating rural communities. If such a policy is applied in regions where agriculture is still largely dependent on natural resources, it will almost certainly fail unless it has previously been shown to be compatible with a very extensive type of land-use. Difficulties arise from the fact that rural communities are wide open to the influences of the political authorities and to mass movements of their population. However, a society's methods of managing and developing its environmental resources are resistant to change and evolve only after a certain lapse of time, the acquisition of wide experience, and the exercise of great caution.

Shortly after 1950, the colonial authorities radically altered their previous policy and encouraged the development of certain tree crops in the original Ngbaka environment. Many villagers became coffee planters, and, after a few years, some individuals were very successful. However, there were signs of several disequilibria. The first was the breakdown of the rational system of resource management because of materially incompatible activities. Coffee trees required care and supervision which did not easily fit in with the lengthy, collective journeys into the forest of the traditional system. Social adjustments were even more difficult. The planter needed the help of young people and of his own wives. If he kept them back forcefully, he had to cope with their unwillingness; if he let them leave for the forest, he was faced with a job which was far too much for him alone. The planter also found it difficult to carry out the obligatory acts of presence and reverence of traditional life, especially if he was young and just beginning to make his own way. Finally, 'he became the odd-man-out in the group, as the other members felt that his attitude was a sign of contempt towards them, and a lack of respect to the memory of their ancestors. The others thought that his conduct meant he denied the fraternal bonds of the lineage' (Thomas 1973). This example illustrates the problem of going from one particular method of using natural resources to another more in line with the new national economy. There is also the problem of the rôle of individual initiatives as agents of the necessary change. This problem occurs in the central area of the Ivory Coast, where it has been considerably aggravated by limitations due to lack of space.

THE BAOULE REGION (IVORY COAST)

The Baoulé region lies slightly to the South and East of the exact centre of the Ivory Coast. It has four salient characteristics: a culturally homogeneous population - the Baoulé people - who settled in this area mostly during the 18th century; high population density compared with other regions of the Ivory Coast (an average 27 inhabitants/km^2 a few years ago, and even more today); a town with more than 100,000 inhabitants (Bouaké), which, in spite of the fact that part of its population comes from the North, includes the majority of the population of the Baoulé region and represents the most important element in the Ivory Coast economy; finally, a natural environment consisting of vast periforest savannas whose Southern edge penetrates the forest zone in the form of a large 'V' (the 'Baoulé V').

From the point of view of human activities, the Baoulé region is a transitional one, a crossing between the forest and savanna zones. The Baoulé people's ability to make use of the particular distribution of natural resources in the vegetation mosaic is reflected in the large variety of cultivated plants. Yams are the dominant crop. The Baoulé people use the distinct particularities of the two species *Dioscorea alata* and *D. cayennensis*. No less than a total of 34 clonal varieties were recorded in three villages (Blanc-Pamard 1975). Next in importance to yams, there are not only manioc, taro (*Xanthosoma* spp.) and sweet potatoes, but also a good many plants with edible seeds (*Dolichos* beans, plants of the Cucurbitaceae family with oil-bearing seeds, groundnuts, maize, rice and even a little sorghum in the North-East of the region). Every type of environment is thus used to grow crops, with the exception of the pure grass savannas at the foot of slopes which have poor soils, and the fringing forests. However, even the most infertile savannas are used for hunting. Hunting seems to have been much more important in the past. The broken boundary between the two major plant formations is used by beaters to make game animals break cover, for hunting animals using fire, and for setting up fences lined with traps. The fringing forests which have not as yet been converted into flooded paddyfields are the realm *par excellence* for the manufacture of palm-wine, because of the many *Raphia* palms and oil-palms. This activity also takes place on a large scale in the fan-palm savannas which are characteristic of the apex of the Baoulé V. The Baoulé people also raise animals – sheep and dwarf goats, and occasionally cattle (there is even a trypano-resistant Baoulé race of cattle intermediate between the N'Dama race and the Lagunes cattle). There are many villages specializing in animal-raising at the Southern end of the Eastern stem of the V, at the edge of a particularly vast stretch of savanna. At Sakassou, there are more cattle than inhabitants (Blanc-Pamard 1975).

The peasant farmer always manages to meet his objectives, at least for food, by manipulating the different species and varieties of yams and their array of accompanying plants, and by choosing the plants growing in the second or sometimes the third year after the main crop. Blanc-Pamard (1975) noted some revealing facts on this subject for three villages at the apex of the Baoulé V. At Tafissou, the cultivated lands lie half in the forest and half in the savanna. The forest food crops are always grown in immature coffee-cocoa plantations, and, in the first year, consist mainly of various varieties of yams giving a single harvest (*D. alata*). These are followed in the second year by rain forest crops, bananas and taros, associated with maize. Yams are then grown on clearings in the savanna, but this time they are clones of the species *Dioscorea cayennensis*, and especially the early-growing Lopka variety which needs staking and gives two harvests. Manioc, which is grown with yams before succeeding it in the crop rotation, is therefore considered a savanna crop. Generally speaking, the savanna yam varieties are preferred to the forest varieties, especially for preparing the Baoulé national dish, *foutou*. In addition, they have the advantage of being immediately ready to eat, whereas the forest yams have to be kept several months on trays in order to harden sufficiently. Villages with few savanna lands, such as Groudji, reserve their savannas lying in the forests for intensive crops of Lopka. Forest edges are very important for growing food crops. The Baoulé people define them as the places where grass and forest meet, 'the foot of the forest' (Blanc-Pamard 1975). If the villagers are to be believed, it is here that the same varieties give the highest yields and have the best flavour. This is why there is such an impressive concentration of plots at forest edges or around the isolated 'islands' of forest. In addition, 'all the fields laid out at forest edges... have a judicious combination of yam varieties, according to whether the mounds face the forest or the savanna' (Blanc-Pamard 1975). When mature coffee and cocoa plantations are dominant, the tendency is to transfer the essential food crops to the savanna: 'the savanna is for food and the forest for making money' (Blanc-Pamard 1975).

The Baoulé people are always looking for things to trade and for ways to make a profit. The savanna was first to provide both. From their contact with the native populations (gradually assimilated into their own) and with their Gouro neighbours, they began to grow cotton, to weave, and then to sell loincloths and blankets. Colonization reduced this to a local, luxury craft activity, while introducing the opportunity of growing cocoa and coffee, a practice which the Baoulé people then adopted.

Thus, in every time and place, the Baoulé people have been able to derive, combine and fit together the elements of a multi-purpose strategy for resources, thanks to a wide range of plants and a good deal of 'savoir-faire'.

This strategy, which uses remarkably few natural resources, contrasts with the strategy

which exhausts rare resources and spreads out
the population, as revealed in the case of the
Ngbaka people. In Baoulé agriculture, the most
exacting task is the construction of the
mounds for growing yams. Calculations made for
seven different villages indicate that between
400 and 1,700 m^3 of earth have been moved to
make between 3,500 and 10,000 mounds per
hectare (Ripailles 1966). Much work is also
involved in staking the early-growing varieties
of yams, but this is in proportion to the
yields: 10 t/ha for late-growing yams; 9.6 and
7.8 t/ha respectively for the two harvests of
early-growing yams. In the second year, the
length of the rainy period makes it possible
to grow two successive crops on the same plot,
e.g. ground-nuts-cotton, or ground-nuts-rice.
In actual fact, in the year following the yam
crop, about 50 per cent of the fields are
abandoned or are used for growing yams during
only one of the two seasons. All things considered, the population needs only very small
areas in order to live, and population density
can rise considerably without reducing the
length of the fallow period. At Adiamprikofikro-
Douakankro, a double village situated 20 km
South-East of Bouaké, each inhabitant cultivates
only 16 ares of yams and another 5 for second-
year secondary crops (Wurtz 1971). Although
the population density is as high as 41 in-
habitants/km^2, only 6 per cent of the total
land surface is cultivated at a time. After
the soil has been used for a maximum of a year
and a half, there is a fallow period lasting
on the average 8.63 years. Recently introduced
cotton and rice crops increase the area under
temporary cultivation and reduce the theoretical
length of the fallow period to about 6 years
for one year's cropping. However, there is still
a great deal of land in reserve: out of 1,041
hectares, only 650 are used in the cropping
cycle. Of the remaining 400 hectares, it is
necessary to substract the area which cannot
be cultivated for edaphic reasons (outcrops
of hard-pan) or for sociological reasons
(sacred forest); however, an appreciable fraction could be recuperated if necessary. These
figures agree with those of the investigations
made at the same period (just before 1965) on
6 villages scattered over the entire Baoulé
region (Ripailles 1966). Yams took up between
7.7 and 15.9 ares per permanent village inhabitant, 'secondary' crops between 0.9 and
14.1 ares; the total area slightly exceeded
25 ares in only one of the six villages. The
limit to the balance between available area
and land requirements seems to have been
reached in two cases, and overstepped in a
third. In the first two cases, population

densities were respectively 60 and 65 inhab-
itants/km^2, and fallow periods between successive yam crops were of 'normal' length, 9 year
in one case and 11 years in the other. In the
third case, the land fed almost 100 inhabitant
km^2, and fallow periods were reduced to about
6 years, which is definitely not long enough.
However, this situation cannot really be consi-
ered critical.

The inhabitants of the 'Béoumi area' North-
East of the Baoulé region have recently been
deprived of the part of their land resources
which now lies submerged under the reservoir
of the dam on the Kossou river. Today, the
sector nearest the water has a population of
more than 120 inhabitants/km^2 (Lassailly 1976)
This 'dense zone' is surrounded by a crescent-
shaped area where the population still exceeds
60 inhabitants/km^2. When there is sufficient
land available, the farmers cultivate between
8 and 11 ares of yams per consumer per year,
which is enough to meet food requirements.
When a greater surface area is cultivated, it
is in order to be able to sell the surplus
produce. Only a fraction of this land is used
in the second year for growing extra food crop
As for the length of the fallow period, from
what the peasant farmers say, it lasts 10 year
for forest lands, and 5-7 years for plots situated in the savanna. The maximum carrying
capacity is calculated at 156 inhabitants/km^2.
Counting the land that is unavailable or used
for cash crops, this corresponds to an overall
population density of about 100 inhabitants/
km^2. When population density exceeds this
figure, or land becomes scarce, three reaction
can be observed to compensate for these effect
Firstly, in spite of the infertile soils, peop
no longer hesitate about cultivating the strip
of grassy savanna bordering the fringing fores
Secondly, cultivation is extended over more tha
two years, and certain plots are cultivated fo
three years and even more. Lastly, the fallow
period is reduced to 4 and even 3 years. This
situation does not seem to be critical in the
immediate future, but in the most populated
villages, resources are reduced to a minimum,
people acquire land in other areas, and some
people start to leave.

The potential natural resources have not
been seriously impoverished, in spite of the
difficulties which started to appear as early
as 1950. Since the work of Monnier (1968), it
is known that the Baoulé savannas would evolve
towards a forest if left to themselves in the
absence of man, or under artificial protection.
More recent research has shown that, far from
arresting natural succession, cultivation, on
the contrary, actually accelerates this process

under certain conditions (Blanc-Pamard and Spichiger 1973). In the Baoulé region, only very exceptional population densities will make the vegetation really regress, leading to savanization. The agricultural system manages to preserve the essential soil resource, although unintentionally, and the climax is definitely a forest type.

Apart from the problem of tree crops, in general the Baoulé people do not lack land. Thus, their policy of accepting newcomers is related to the fact that their land is under-exploited and under-occupied. In the Béoumi area, the farmer 'can very well ask for the right to cultivate either lands in other wards or the lands lying at the territorial border' (Lassailly 1976). This flexible land-tenure regime formerly facilitated village dispersion during the initial phase of settlement. Today, it favours the trend of setting up coffee-cocoa plantations; it enables those who have lost their lands to re-establish themselves; and it makes it possible to set aside land necessary for development projects or for modernizing agriculture. It is as if the Baoulé society were still living under the impetus of the old social strategy of competition by population numbers, which gave impetus to the assembly of migrants during the first centuries, and to the massive purchases of slaves at the end of the 19th century.

The Baoulé people also have a certain strategy behind their movements. It is a long time since the Baoulé society, as a whole, stopped migrating. It now has solid roots and has established its territory on two different levels. On the one hand, the main groups have made 'federations' occupying zones of continuous settlement separated by strips of land 5 to 10 km wide, deliberately left empty. On the other hand, within each of these zones, each village controlled, and still controls, its cultivated 'territory'. However, although territorial limits have been fixed, there is still a considerable amount of migration. As it exists today, this migration does not correspond to excessive pressure on agricultural resources, but generally arises from personal desire for independence and wealth. The Baoulé society is very much marked by this point of view; in the villages, the basic social unit, the *aoulo*, or vaguely defined group of blood relatives, is centred around the 'treasure' and its keeper (Etienne and Etienne 1966). This is contrary to Mossi social practice, for example, where a rich man has a recognized authority. There have been two major movements of Baoulé society, in the conditions mentioned above. The first was related to the discovery of gold-placers near Dimbokro and Toumodi, and took the form of a sort of gold rush towards the forest regions of the South from the end of the 18th century (de Salverte-Marmier and de Salverte-Marmier 1966). The much more recent second movement was the outcome of the reorientation of the Baoulé trading economy to coffee and cocoa production. This time the migrants went much further afield in the search for suitable soils for these crops. Colonization first took place in the patches of forest within the central Baoulé region (Trouchaud 1966). The pioneer fronts of these tree crops were then moved to the edge of the Baoulé territory. The current phase is the penetration of large sectors of the Ivory Coast forest; the Baoulé people infiltrate and settle in the midst of other peoples, and today they have almost reached the Atlantic Ocean in the San Pedro region. In the case of coffee and cocoa, as well as for gold, it is not the land as such that attracts - or attracted - the migrants, but rather very localized resources. There are many villages which have hardly enough forest to set up even a few hectares of plantations. Even in the most unsuitable areas, such as the Western stem of the V, settlement took place at such a rate in the 1950s (when prices were highest, i.e. before the present period), that many planters soon found they could not extend the planted area any further. They could only 'revise' their plantation with great difficulty and at great cost, or more generally leave altogether. In addition, cocoa and coffee trees have insufficient rainfall in the Baoulé country. This means that the drought of recent years has been a catastrophe. Many factors explain why there are such differences between localities and why migration is directed to one region and then another: soil type and water-retaining properties; geographical position in relation to isohyets; and local composition of the vegetation mosaic. The rate of spread of 'plantations' is such that the areas of forest assigned as 'camps' by the first people to arrive - Baoulé or non-Baoulé - are quickly saturated (Blanc-Pamard 1975). The owners of the plantations that are 'finished' then go further afield in search of new areas to be developed. The inverse also happens; the savanna villages contain many planters who have returned home, but who obtain at least part of their income from the cocoa and coffee trees left far behind in the forest in the care of a family member. Individual itineraries are thus marked out by plantations from the North to the South in a way reminiscent of the situation in Ghana - but in an East-West direction - for the planters originating from Akwapim.

This strategy of land-use and land development implies that, in theory, providing the Baoulé peasant can expect to make a good profit, he is available for any operation using natural resources. It was thus that the idea came about to settle the peasant farmers forced to move because of the Kossou reservoir on the 'new lands' of the South-West Ivory Coast, inland from the new port of San Pedro. Of the 75,000 people who had to move when the reservoir was filled, it was expected that 65,000 would leave for the South-West, but barely 4,000 accepted this move. The solution was therefore to be found in a completely different direction: resettlement in the neighbouring area, with an adequate system for organizing agricultural land-use. This involves a very different strategy.

Until the beginning of the 1970s, the Ivory Coast had a State policy aiming essentially at increasing production. Important specialized companies were set up at the national level to organize the peasant farmers, which they often did with great efficiency: the Société d'amélioration technique et de modernisation agricole en Côte d'Ivoire (Company for Technical Development and Agricultural Modernization in the Ivory Coast) for tree crops; the Compagnie ivoirienne des fibres textiles (Ivory Coast Company for Textile Fibres) for cotton. Companies which would later be transformed into co-operatives were set up in a certain number of villages. An ultra-modern factory for processing and conditioning coffee, constructed not far from the Kossou dam, began to operate in the 1970s. However, the concept of planned resource management was largely absent from these actions, which were directed at an unorganized peasant farming society. Management of natural resources in the Baoulé region really began with the spread of flooded paddyfield rice cultivation, which, until 1960, was limited to very small areas. A large-scale project was directed by the Société pour le développement de la riziculture (Company for the Development of Rice Cultivation), a State company like the others. The considerable increase in the national purchase price of rice in 1975 contributed towards its success.

The Autorité de la vallée du Bandama (Bandama Valley Authority), responsible for all activities connected with the Kossou dam and hydro-electric works, undertook various projects which were much more spectacular. The essential problem concerning the reservoir was to provide a living, within a region that was already well-populated, for the thousands of families dispossessed of their lands and plantations. The solutions that were applied were the first attempts in the Baoulé region at setting up an integrated system making better use of the natural resources than traditional agriculture had (Lassailly 1976). New villages were constructed in a very open checker-board or concentric alignment pattern. The inhabitants of the villages that were submerged, or about to be submerged, were rehoused in appropriate localities, especially to the East and the South of the reservoir. The transposed villages were usually grouped together to form units of about a thousand inhabitants. Collective facilities have helped raise social standards. From the point of view of agriculture, however, only part of the rehoused population has been absorbed in various types of modern farming activities, for example the blocks of annual crops. Each block of about 150 ha (usually held by one person) is divided into five fields for crop rotation separated by windrows for controlling erosion. The crops are rotated as follows: yams, maize followed by cotton, rice, and the last two years grazed fallow of *Stylosanthes gracilis*. The participants receive a hectare in each field, i.e. five hectares in all. In return for paying expenses, they can benefit from a whole series of motorized equipment under collective management, a system which is very widespread. The trypanoresistant cattle are collectively owned; the young cattle, about 100 per block, are fattened within 18 months. Subtracting expenses and personal consumption, the average income per person should reach 170,000 CFA francs (US $340) net per year, i.e. much more than the same annual crops produced in the traditional environment. The operation is successful technically speaking. However, should it be considered as a model for future management of natural resources? It should be noted that, until 1976, the 32 cropping areas covering 5,000 ha have only been able to receive a total of 1,100 families, in spite of their size and the amount of money invested. Owing to the force of circumstances, inequalities arose between the old and the new inhabitants, and even within the villages with the rehoused peasant farmers. The distribution of natural resources was even more seriously affected by this same inequality. The dispossessed villagers were mainly sent to the 'Béoumi area', i.e. the most populated part. The necessary land was therefore taken from an already partially 'overpopulated' area. Certain cultivated lands were seriously reduced in size, sometimes losing over 25 per cent of the workable area. This created a scarcity of land, which had different repercussions, as the people of the most populated areas close to the reservoir moved out quite far towards the periphery, setting up camps and fields of crops on land that was still unappropriated. As for the block system, it remains to be seen whether the users will adapt over time to the greater amount of work (562 days work per family per year against 472 in the traditional system), and to the strict regulation of the agricultural timetable; or whether they consider it as a means of making money. What is certain is that the re-settled farmers borrow land from the inhabitants of the old villages, which they cultivate in traditional-type plots along with their own share of the blocks. The lands cultivated outside the blocks cover over a third of the area worked by the resident peasant farmers. They are used particularly for growing crops that are absent from the obligatory crop rotation of the blocks, such as early varieties of yams, an irreplaceable local food. It can be noted that under a series of names - crops grown 'outside the zone', 'outside the plots', or 'outside the peasant farmed area' - such fields can be found everywhere where the land is cultivated in a geometrical lay-out, under the direction of government authorities. This means that there is an error of co-ordination between the two strategies; one which organizes natural resources in a strict pattern in time and space, the other by which societies maintain a necessary margin of freedom and uncertainty.

LESSONS FROM A DEBATABLE STRATEGY: THE AGRICULTURAL 'ALLOTMENTS' IN THE FORMER BELGIAN CONGO

In the preceding example of the semi-mechanized block cropping system in the Ivory Coast, a modern strategy was used to create a new system alongside the old one, which continued to function according to traditional standards in the remaining intervals of land. If the new system flourishes and the old one dies out, there would be a process of substitution taking place. However, a different system could be envisaged where the new system relies on the old one in order to transform it. This is what agronomists tried to do on a large scale in the former Belgian Congo. Hundreds of thousands of 'peasant farmers' were taken on during the last years before Independence; this project was, however, literally obliterated following the departure of the colonist government. Nevertheless, it is still a rich source of information for present-day Africa. It would be worthwhile for more people to know about this project, not only to avoid repeating the same errors, as occasionally happens in different political contexts, but also because the mass

of information and ideas involved contain many elements that could be relevant for a strategy for resources management in regions where extensive agriculture is practised, that is in or near the dense, moist forest zone.

The Plan décennal du Congo (Congo Ten-Year Plan) for the period 1950-1960 aimed at making 440,000 families into 'peasant farming households'. As it concerned rural societies whose production system usually depended on temporary cropping, the terms 'peasant farmer' and 'paysannat' (peasant farming community) emphasized that the main objective was to settle the population on the land. The 'agricultural allotments' within the general context of the 'paysannats' were both the most important and the most resistant feature of the project.

This project involved the so-called Bantu farming system based on 'minimum soil treatment and preparation, a short cropping cycle with a variety of plants, and a long period during which the land was allowed to lie fallow, the length of time of which vary in different regions' (Staner 1955). This system was adapted to a certain number of major principles: avoiding wastage of soil resources; facilitating and accelerating the transition from collective land control to individual ownership, along with the concept of 'gradual development of the individual and of his sense of initiative' (Staner 1955); increasing the productivity of agricultural work, so as to end food scarcities and discourage rural depopulation by providing a steady, relatively high income; facilitating the farmers' technical training by allowing the same person to supervise more fields; finally, encouraging the changeover to mechanized, intensive agriculture.

Action was limited first of all to 'rationalizing and regulating the much discredited nomadic cropping methods' (Staner 1955). Therefore, it was immediately decided that the African farmers should not copy the European model of agriculture. It is interesting to note that this idea has reappeared in international thinking. The project first began in 1936 when the agronomists of Gandajika in the peri-forest savannas of the Southern Congo Basin decided to install five local cultivators on 9 ha plots. They could cultivate the land for their own benefit, using the methods recommended by the agronomical research services (INEAC). However, at the beginning of the last war, the important cotton companies were quick to pick up the idea. The final project was a compromise between the two strategies: the technicians' strategy, steeped in authoritative paternalism; and the companies' strategy, with one-sided interests. Although the cotton companies cannot be held totally responsible for the project's failure, they had a great deal to do with unbalancing the system and generally causing it to fail at such an early date.

The basic principle behind the 'agricultural allotments' was connected with the way in which the cultivated area was geometrically laid out both for distributing land amongst the cultivators, and as a means for organizing land-use over time. The social structure of the population units was in theory left untouched. Each village group found itself attributed with one or several 'blocks' cleared in the savanna or the forest. These blocks were in turn divided into plots, the size of which corresponded to what a healthy man, helped by his family, was supposed to be able to cultivate in a given year; the plot area varied between 30 and 50 ares. In the first year, all the plots were cleared of vegetation. They were all placed side by side along a straight line, which in the forest, ran West to East, so as to provide the crops with maximum light. The plots cleared in the second year formed a row parallel with the first, and so on. Each row was made of as many plots as there were cultivators in the block. There were as many rows as years in the cropping-fallow cycle, originally established by the agronomists; for example, there were 20 rows for a total of five years cropping followed by 15 years fallow.

There were definite reasons for setting the plots up in rows. They saved time for the person responsible for controlling the blocks and supervising the type and the condition of the crops; this lay-out also made it possible to eventually spray insecticides and use mechanized equipment. In the forest, the linear clearings were narrow enough to facilitate regrowth, thus giving a good start to the fallow period. In order to encourage forest regrowth even more, clearings were often made in alternate rather than contiguous strips, using the 'culture en couloirs' method (corridor cultivation). Another variation was to make pairs of strips side by side, alternating with strips that were either uncleared, or else already overgrown by forest; a banana plantation made the division between the double 'corridors'. In the savanna, another method consisted in cultivating the first row of the rotation, and then the last, so as to contain the whole block within two fire-breaks. However, if the cultivated clearings were immoderately long in relation to their width, the fields were prone to damage by wild animals, and there was an increase in the effect that the edges had on lowering yields. The solution was then to widen the rows, by elongating the plots.

Irrespective of the pattern of land-clearing the plots successively cropped by the same cultivator were lined up end to end, forming one person's share. It was planned that, in the following cycle, each cultivator, or his successor, would return to the plots he had first cleared. The plots were thus permanently allocated. It was expected that in time, a bond would be established between the cultivators and the plots of land which they had cleared, which they would then get used to considering their own. This would be a step towards real land appropriation, and, with more intensive cropping, the beginning of a small, settled 'paysannat', which was the whole aim of the project.

From the beginning, 'stabilized' shifting cultivation involved not only organizing the lay-out of the various plots, but also the timing of the various cropping practices. In the forest areas where land was abundant, the preliminary trials maintained the lengthy fallow periods of traditional agriculture. On the other hand, the blocks where successive crops were grown over several years replaced the single crop, or the crop harvested over two years, as was characteristic of the Bantu system. In one of the oldest 'paysannats' with agricultural allotments, the farmers respected the following crop rotation: Year 1, 10 ares of rice in the first season, plus the food crop association (maize, beans, marrows) on the rest of the plot, i.e. 40 ares; cotton in the second season, but only on 40 ares as it takes too long to replace rice. Year 2: ground-nuts in the first season, cotton in the second. Year 3: bananas and manioc. Year 4: manioc and banana harvest. Year 5: end of banana harvest. From Years 6 to 18, the crops are replaced by fallow (De Coene 1956). However, the 4th and 5th years are transition periods, when the soil is no longer worked and the natural vegetation starts to grow back. It can therefore be calculated that the land lies fallow for 15 out of the 18 years of the full cycle. This succession of crops is quite typical: on the one hand, the succession ends with crops which take a long time to grow; on the other hand, cash crops are relatively important, notably cotton, which is grown on no less than 90 ares per year per individual plot.

One of the acknowledged intentions of the project of agricultural allotments was to free the villagers from the 'customary jurisdiction' (masters of the land, clan chiefs, etc.), which was considered an obstacle to any kind of change There was indeed an enormous difference between land-use under the old and the new systems. Many legal disputes arose, some the very day the land was shared out amongst the cultivators, for whom the local laws no longer applied, sometimes two or three years after the allotments were established. In certain cases, it was necessary to reinstate the rôle of the master of the land and his council, so as to avoid any disputes concerning how the blocks were set up and the plots allocated. This meant that the dignitaries who were most resistant to any changes and to the development of individual land ownership were once more held in esteem.

Of course, the geometrical lay-out of this strategy of resource management was incompatible with natural environmental diversity. It could have been possible to avoid this problem by not giving out the poor quality plots, but this would have upset the order of the cultivated strips, and individual shares of land would no longer lie in a straight line. In the Kivu hilly regions, the solution was to abandon the principle of dividing the land using straight lines, and to use contour lines instead. Generally speaking, it was difficult to set up the blocks because of variations in soil quality and plant cover. It was necessary to find a uniform area of land sufficiently large. Sometimes the blocks had to be set up far away from the villages, which meant that the cultivators had to make long journeys back and forth.

On the other hand, in 'setting standard measurements for the areas of land to be cleared', the project inevitably neglected 'all the relationships which existed between firstly, the surface area cleared of vegetation, and secondly, the composition of the peasant's family, his working capacity, and his determination' (Béguin 1960). In other words, this meant 'ignoring a village's characteristic diversity'. There was a great range of physical strength and needs according to the age, health, and marital status of the participants. For example, bachelors found it difficult to cultivate the same area as families would. One general method for avoiding these difficulties was used in the peasant farming communities near the Yangambi agronomical station in the heart of the forest. In this case, the cultivators were not allocated with fixed areas along the cultivated 'corridors'. Every year, the land to be cleared was distributed differently amongst the interested parties according to the available manpower. However, this type of allotment, which is usually referred to as 'collective' or 'semi-collective', could not be used for developing the 'peasant farming philosophy' which was the project's main objective.

Another aberration noticed in the 1950s was that a great many crops were grown outside the blocks. Béguin (1960) studied an area of 2,300 km^2 with 74,000 inhabitants in Kasaï, where the 'peasant farmers' formed only 40 per cent of the households, and not quite half the total population. There are various reasons for such a situation, fairly similar to those noted at Béoumi: people wanting additional crops which were not included in the rotations and the concern for initiative and independence. In addition, it was a good safety measure to participate in both the traditional and the introduced systems. The allotments eventually were allowed to fall apart, as indicated by the aerial photographs and detailed surveys (Tulippe 1955).

The government authorities had to revise their objectives. Although by the end of 1953 more than 100,000 families had settled, the people responsible for the project felt that matters were getting out of hand. 'In 1955–1956, it became necessary to take a break and to review the situation' (Anon. 1960). Decolonization helped to hasten the failure of the system.

The general reason behind this failure is connected to the inflexibility of the allotment system, the unpleasant pressure associated with the setting up of the system, and finally, the effort that the cultivators had to put into the project without what they considered sufficient returns. It was found that the system's inflexibility was incompatible with the social context as well as with 'the diversity of the physical and biological environment' (Béguin 1960).

Nevertheless, it is very difficult to assess to what extent these operations were obligatory. People could 'freely and individually' choose to join the peasant farming community, 'although encouraged by propaganda' (Béguin 1960). But to what point did propaganda insist that people join the project? This is the whole question. Before setting up the plots, the 'customary chiefs' were asked for their opinion. There was a whole series of consultations of the 'village palaver' type. However, could these traditional dignitaries refuse? Tulippe (1955) spoke of how, 'in some areas, pressure had to be applied to the chiefs or the native population, whether they liked it or not', and in this he saw 'one of the most delicate parts of the operation'. Moreover, although people refused to join the allotments, this did not necessarily mean that they had a negative attitude towards work, nor to an increase in their income. Nevertheless, a certain amount of obligation existed in the 'obligatory crops of the crop rotations. The geometrical lay-out developed on the basis of this strategy of resource management, although *a priori* neutral with respect to the authoritative system, nevertheless became deeply implicated. Certain allotments were used for growing coffee, or surplus foodstuffs to supply the population centres. However, under the pressure of capitalistic interests, the crops were organized so as to particularly favour cotton production. In terms of time and allotted space, cotton received the most and the best. The cotton fields required the most work, but they were a relatively low source of income for the 'peasant farmer'. Detailed calculations at Fuladu, at the Northern limits of the main forest region, show that cotton brought in 0.65 Congolese francs per hour of work. This is hardly more than for rice or ground-nuts (of which a small portion was sold), and much less than what was earned harvesting palm fruits, 2.20 francs/hour (de Smet and Huysecom-Wolter 1972).

THE OIL-PALM: A RESOURCE FOR MANY STRATEGIES

The oil-palm, *Elaeis guineensis,* is a forest species originating in Africa. It is, however, a light-loving plant, whose original habitat seems to have been the banks of rivers or lakes and the edges of certain natural clearings. The oil-palm grove is a man-made plant formation as it is a secondary forest with a greater proportion of oil-palms. The distribution of this species is governed by rainfall. The most Northern palm groves (the *niayes* of the 'petite côte' (small coast) to the North-East of Dakar, the Mandoul basin in Southern Chad) are most certainly relics of a past moist climatic phase. In addition, there is a correlation between the areas where they grow in abundance (and tend to invade like weeds), and the areas with deep sandy soils. In Bénin, for example, or Togo, 'the supreme areas for oil-palms are without a doubt the plateaux of 'terres de barres' (bar soils)'(Mondjannagni 1970). It is worth noting that some of the regions where oil-palms are most abundant lie on the fringe of this species' distribution as limited by rainfall (1,500-1,600 mm/yr). This is the case of the Kwilu region, the main oil-palm growing area of Zaire, and also of the coastal zone of Togo and Bénin, where annual rainfall varies between 1,350 and 1,150 mm. Young *Elaeis* plants growing in cleared sites at the limit of the dense moist forest are more resistant to competition from other species than when growing in the midst of the forest.

An oil-palm grove is obtained fairly quickly when ecological conditions are suitable and cropping is repeated from forest clearing to forest clearing at more or less regular intervals. For this, it is sufficient that the existing *Elaeis* are left standing when the forest is cleared, and they then reproduce freely.

Nevertheless, this process is to a greater or lesser extent intentional. The Bassa people of Cameroun (Eséka region) have an oil-palm oriented economy, and palms are grown around the family farms, thus constituting a palm grove several hectares in size. Two cropping cycles are necessary to bring tree density up to 50-70/ha. In populated regions, a stand of oil-palms associated with shrub-covered fallow land generally evolves towards a 'palm grove park', of which the most typical examples are found around Porto Novo (Bénin) (Mondjannagni 1970). A very similar landscape is found on a much larger scale in the central part of Eastern Nigeria; from Enugu to Uyo to Port Harcourt, the eye is greeted by a veritable sea of *Elaeis*. Associated within this formation, as around Porto Novo, there are a palm grove park, particularly well managed and fertilized crops, and a housing pattern that is both dense and dispersed. This is one of the most populated regions of the country: more than 350 inhabitants/km^2 within a strip of land nearly 200 km long and 40-50 km wide.

There is therefore 'a complete series of landscapes, reconstituting all the stages between the virgin forest and the monospecific palm grove, representing the transformation of forest wildlands into a park through increasingly selective forest clearing in favour of one crop' (Pélissier 1963). Tjeega (1974) described how the Bassa farms are surrounded by three concentric rings: in the centre, the oil-palm grove proper, exploited regularly, but without food crops; then an open palm grove (15-25 trees/ha) associated with temporary fields renewed every five to six years; finally, over a kilometer away, an area of forest scattered with unexploited oil-palms. In Eastern Nigeria, as the population density of the Ibo-Ibibio people increases, the cropped area under the oil-palm park is expanded, and, past a certain limit of population density, the village clusters join together in a continuous palm grove.

Within the context of a market economy, an unquestionable amount of damage has been done by abusive exploitation of oil-palms, particularly by felling trees for making palm wine (resulting in authoritative prohibitory measures which ignored the relationships between forest societies and their environment). However, there are also many cases showing how oil-palms tend to invade every piece of land. The forest cultivators do not just encourage oil-palm reproduction; for a long time they have planted them as well: the Abomey palm grove in Bénin was originally created at the initiative of the Ghezo and Glélé kings (Mondjannagni 1977). At the present time, a real palm grove vine-yard is being developed on the Eastern Togo and Western Bénin plateaux, and on either side of the Mono River. In many fields, the palm seedlings are being planted in regular rows in the middle of maize and manioc. Some of the trees are felled once a new cropping cycle is begun after a fallow period. The surviving trees disappear in their turn during a third and last cycle. In the Anfouin region of Togo, the oil-palms are not even given time to grow. They are burnt during an almost continuous cropping cycle, which is associated with pop-ulation densities of over 200 and even 300 in-habitants/km^2.

Generally speaking, the traditional strat-egy for dealing with oil-palms consisted of going along with, and sometimes making adjust-ments in the naturally-occurring process, rather than deliberately altering nature. Pop-ulation numbers are the driving force: the map of palm groves corresponds fairly well to the map of population density (Nicolaï 1963). This species grows so vigorously in its eco-logically favourable regions that its propaga-tion cannot be checked by even excessive ex-ploitation. However, in the aging, garden palm groves, the old trees take up space and com-plicate harvesting.

In the forest regions or the Guinea savannas, people find that the oil-palm is a particularly useful tree, and are agents in its propagation. In the Bassa area (Cameroun), 'nothing is neglected (in the oil-palm),... from the palm fronds to the fruits to the trunk itself' (Tjeega 1974). However, it is most important as a source of food. The kernels are eaten with taros cooked over a charcoal fire; the mushrooms which grow on the heaps of shells left over after extraction of the palm oil are harvested and eaten; the oil-palm worms (*Rhyn-cophorus phoenicis*) are also eaten. The main products are wine, made by drawing off the sap and leaving it to ferment naturally, and oil, which is extracted from the pericarp of the fruits.

The importance of oil-palms as a resource is shown on two different levels. First of all, it is highly valued both culturally and social-ly. Palm wine facilitates relationships between people, is a mark of good-will, and is used in benedictions. The Bakongo people of the Braz-zaville region have a whole pattern of conduct based upon wine, which was once only harvested by men who could be relied on, hiers apparent to those who had authority at the head of lineage-based groups.

In Bénin and Togo, the products of the natural palm grove still represent 'an important source of export revenue' (Machioudi Dissou 1972). In Eastern Nigeria, the cultivators derive most of their money from oil-palms, as this country is one of the world's greatest exporters of palm oil and palm kernels. Accord-ing to Floyd (1969), a few years ago 40 per cent of oil production was obtained by rudiment-ary methods (by foot and by hand), and 50 per cent by manual screw-presses, with only 10 per cent coming from modern installations. The economy of the Bassa area in Cameroun 'from the monetary point of view, still largely depends on the exploitation of natural and sub-natural palm groves' (Tjeega 1974).

The oil-palm has the special characteristic of 'making a very good bridge between the so-called traditional economy and a money-based economy' (Tjeega 1974). Modern exploitation has to cope with social customs and traditional institutions. For example, around 1950, the Adioukrou people of the Ebrié lagoon, West of Abidjan, numbering about 25,000, continued to practise the same kind of economy after the second world war as they did a century earlier. They then used to sell palm oil to the European ships calling in at Jacqueville or Grand-Jack. The palm groves were regenerated with the minimum of care. However, the former procedures and regulations for controlling appropriation of land bearing palm trees, harvesting fruit and oil extraction, were still largely applied. Palm grove exploitation was regulated by strictly allocating the various tasks according to age-classes of eight year intervals. The two youngest classes of adults were the tree climbers, the third cut down branches, and the fourth inspected the work. All or part of the proceeds went into a collective fund, which was especially used for paying taxes. Two noteworthy characteristics made the Adioukrou society stand out amongst others. Firstly, work was carried out and organized so as to convert a semi-natural resource into material goods and money, which was closely linked with a social strategy based on 'the acquisition of riches and showing them off' (Dupire and Boutillier 1958). The second characteristic is the fact that the society had been so rationally restructured on the basis of usable resources that the procedures established during the 19th century period of economic exchange were still operational a century later.

Fairly similar characteristics were recorded in research on the 'oil rivers' of the East Niger delta, and of the Cross River area. As with the Adioukrou people, the Nigerian coastal societies emphasize the importance of riches and economic power. The 'trading rivers', which became the 'oil rivers' in the 19th century, were organized into States. Each State disposed of both its own territory and 'a trading empire consisting of a certain number of waterways with access to the markets of the hinterland' (Jones 1963). Conflicts arose because these States wanted to control this access and defend the monopoly of the river traffic which concerned them. In the case of the 'oil river states', the strategy for a resource evolved towards territorial control, and it became a strategy in the political sense.

The societies' freedom of action has been very much limited through colonization, fixed national boundaries and modern State arbitration. Today, strategies have been reduced to combining the various productions based on oil-palms in the best possible way. Harvesting wine by tapping the tree at the base of the inflorescence seems to even improve oil yields as it necessitates cleaning up the trees and clearing the surrounding vegetation. However, specialization is inevitable up to a certain point. The new factor in this respect is that urban markets have become very important. The cities demand not only oil from local presses, but also wine and its derivatives. According to Moby-Etia (1976), it is more profitable to sell wine than palm fruits or even oil. In Cameroun, according to official statistics, wine is transported to Douala by tens of thousands of hecto-liters per year. The sale of alcohol is even more profitable than selling wine: the sap of a single oil-palm tree converted into alcohol brings in 2,250 CFA francs locally, and 3,000 ($12) wholesale at Douala. In the form of wine, the profit would have been only 600 and 2,100 francs respectively. As for the fruit, the production of one tree, spread over the whole year, is worth 750 francs. The same trend towards the production of alcohol, catastrophic in many respects, is seen everywhere in Southern Bénin and South-East Togo.

In conclusion, the main advantage of the traditional palm grove is that its exploitation is 'extremely flexible' (Antheaume 1972). According to the needs of the moment, it is considered as capital which has been saved up and which regularly gives interest. This is the case of exploitation for oil. Oil is collected twice a year, and 'represents a stable source of income, partly used for everyday expenses' (Antheaume 1972). However, the palm grove also represents assets 'which can be used for important and unforeseen expenses (funerals, ceremonies, etc.)' (Antheaume 1972).

III. MODERN STRATEGIES AND THEIR CONTRADICTIONS

Today, as in the 19th century, there is a demand for oil-palm products on the world market: firstly, for oil, extracted in the country of origin; secondly, for palm kernels, exported after shelling to be processed generally in the importing countries. Mechanical processing of palm fruits in industrial-type oil presses will be considered as the criteria making the transition from a traditional economy to a modern economy. The only problem is to regularly supply the installations in quantity and quality so as to make them profitable.

Since the beginning of the colonial regime, governments and investors in many countries, but especially in Africa, have had their attention drawn to the reputedly 'natural' palm groves. This was the case of the Kwilu palm groves (South-West Zaïre), studied by Nicolaï (1963). As early as 1911, the Belgian authorities accorded a subsidiary company of the Lever group with the monopoly of purchases in the areas supplying these factories, on condition that they set up a certain number of factories. Other less important companies did the same between the two wars. The system depended on using a great many tree cutters: 40,000 before decolonization, i.e. one man in five within the region's limits. The government paid them a fixed price for the fruits they supplied. Thousands of kilometers of roads were laid down to serve the dense network of trading posts. The Kwilu palm grove was exploited with very little change up to 1960. Urged by the State, the oil companies made a late effort to develop real plantations, which hardly provided more than one sixth of their supply. The companies did manage to make a profit, however; as for the tree cutters, with earnings on the order of 6,500 to 7,000 Congolese francs, they were relatively well off for the standards of the time. Nevertheless, the system functioned in rather artificial conditions. Almost 50 per cent of the cutters were hired from the plateaux in the South where palm groves were absent, and were thus working two or three hundred kilometers from their homes. They were organized in a highly restrictive manner, and even for those who stayed in the village, they did not lose much by leaving.

After the last war, the authorities tried to increase the production of the so-called natural palm groves. In Eastern Nigeria, a 'Palm Grove Rehabilitation Scheme', programmed for the years 1962–1968, managed to renovate 25,000 ha (Floyd 1969). Several other countries made the same kind of effort to renew the palm stands and introduce high-yielding varieties. In most cases, these interventions were accompanied by setting up modern oil presses and creating a road network for collecting palm products by lorry. The oil companies of the Congo had established a highly directive organization, which was replaced by only a collective variation of the same, the palm tree owners being asked to deliver their palm fruits instead of processing them themselves. In the Ivory Coast, the first plan for development after the war programmed setting up an oil press at Dabou. Work was undertaken 'in order to develop, regenerate and extend' the Adioukrou palm grove which was to supply it (Dupire and Boutillier 1958). In Dahomey, starting from 1947, the Service Rénovation Palmeraie (Palm Grove Rehabilitation Service) had 'the delicate task of rehabilitating the aged natural stands situated in areas supplying existing factories and factories that were going to be built' (Machioudi Dissou 1972), of which there were four. It was thus that it was possible to renovate a small part of the Porto Novo palm grove. However, on the whole, this intervention was a miserable failure because of soil exhaustion and 'the peasants' categorical refusal to destroy the old, barely productive trees, which hindered the growth of the selected seedlings. In addition, the peasants were wary of this operation carried out by a government service, which, from their point of view, would take possession of their lands once the new, high-yielding generation of palms started to be productive' (Machioudi Dissou 1972). The Moanda palm grove in the South of Gabon was another catastrophic failure. This had been developed and equipped at great expense for a level of oil production which remained very much below the predicted amounts; the oil press had to rapidly close down. The same thing happened in Cameroun. This almost generalized failure is certainly in part due to the characteristics of the natural palm grove itself. It is non-uniform, dispersed, filled with brush, often aged, and has an insufficient tree density. Therefore by definition it has a low production potential in relation to its area. It is very well suited

to traditional-type exploitation. However, a modern oil press needs perfectly regular supplies to make it pay. This cannot be assured without the help of an authority compelling co-operation, or else with total consent and considerable tenacity on the part of the suppliers. This problem is not confined to natural palm groves, but occurs in all strategies which try to associate parties having radically different constraints, interests and habits in the same production process.

Another modern strategy is to create industrial plantations. In Africa, Cameroun and the Ivory Coast give the best examples of large oil-palm plantations. The palm groves of Cameroun are quite old. They are situated at the foot of Mt. Cameroun in the Western part of the country and they are exploited by a private company and a State company. The Ivory Coast plantations are, on the contrary, fairly recent. From 1963 to 1972, 60,000 ha were planted: production should rise from 68,000 t of oil in 1972 to 250,000 t in about 1980. The plantations are set out in nine agro-industrial complexes which are situated in a narrow strip along the coast. They come under the responsibility of a group of State companies. This enterprise is not only a financial success; it has also carried out a strategy for developing basic natural resources in poorly-populated or uninhabited regions. In Cameroun, oil-palms grow essentially on volcanic soils. On the other hand, in the Ivory Coast they flourish in the sandy soils which are not really suitable for the majority of cash crops. However, it is necessary to find the men for developing and exploiting the palm plantations. The only solution is to bring in the necessary manpower. It was not difficult to attract workmen in Cameroun as the highly populated Bamenda plateau forms the hinterland of the plantation area. For its part, the Ivory Coast called upon the help of immigrants from Upper Volta, but many others also want to employ them. Another problem arose due to the accumulation of people at the edges of the plantations. In Cameroun, when the workers left the plantations, some moved away, others remained there in the urban centres or on the limited land that was left. There was more land in the Ivory Coast, but conditions are difficult for foreigners who wish to settle down.

After attempts had failed to integrate village harvests with a modern production system, a hybrid system was tried, where the peasant combined his activity as producer with industrial processing of palm fruits.

First of all, there were family plantations of selected palms. In Cameroun, at this period

the project consisted in 'creating plantations
free of charge for the peasants who applied
for this to be done on their traditional lands.
All the work (land clearing, staking out, dig-
ging holes, transporting and planting seedlings) was undertaken at the expense of the
Secteur de Modernisation de la palmeraie
(Division for Palm Grove Modernization) (Moby-
Etia 1976). This Division went as far as maintaining the young plantation free of charge
during the first three or four years. However,
'ownership of the plantation reverts back to
the traditional proprietor as soon as it
becomes profitable'. From 1952 to 1958, 846 ha
of family plantations were created around
Dibombari. However, the new planters grew
tired of maintaining their plots, and left
them to themselves. The purchase price of
fruits, considered as being far too low, errors in management, and non-participation
explain why the plantations were abandoned.
This project was taken up again in 1959-1960,
however, giving the participants a more active
rôle. Another few hundred hectares of palm
trees were planted. However, the factory had
to close in 1963 after having functioned at
less than half capacity.

Bénin likewise had a period with individual
plantations, but the idea of grouping the
peasants' plantations into blocks, also associated with industrial oil presses, quickly
predominated. Most interventions took the form
of massive areas of plantations, and over
200,000 ha were planted in this way. The peasants were organized into groups of beneficiary
participants. Within these co-operatives, a
complex system of salaries distinguished the
original owners from the workers who did a minimum number of days' work. The two categories
could be combined. Results have remained very
much below what was hoped, in spite of the
considerable amount of investment, the attention paid in technical aspects in setting up
the plantations, and the elaborate system of
participation.

Until now, the only programme which has met
the expectations of its organizers is that of
the village plantations in the Ivory Coast
(Pillet-Schwartz 1973), really a mixture of
programmes combining individual and co-operative palm groves and agro-industrial blocks.
The production of the latter ensures that the
factories function steadily. The fruits from
the village plantations provide an additional
supply. All palm production is bought up by
the factories, which organize collection as
well as the planters' technical training. At
the end of 1972, there were already 5,000
individual planters over an area of 20,000 ha.

With the planned rate of expansion, the individual planters should supply 40 per cent of
the factories' production at the end of the
1970s. The real village planters (since this
term covers a great many employees, and even
city dwellers) have run into difficulties. They
can no longer manage to devote the time necessary for their trees, as they are taken up by
other activities imposed on them by the society
and local customs. In addition, the lands converted into palm groves are often taken from
the common ancestral territory of a lineage-
based group, therefore at the expense of the
other group members. In spite of the planters'
difficulties and their delicate position between
two societies with conflicting demands, the
project is on the whole a success, and can
surely be taken into account in evaluating the
country's general level of development.

This kind of 'hybrid strategy' almost always
causes problems. The individual or collectively
grouped palm groves have to be inserted firstly
in the land-tenure and land-use systems, which
involve a complex set of social relationships,
and secondly in the process of oil manufacture,
which has strict technical and economic limitations. In connection with the collective
plantations of selected palms on the Sakété
plateau (Bénin), Pélissier (1963) quite rightly
mentioned 'the difficulty of getting round the
conflict between any efforts at planning production, the disorderly land-tenure structure,
and the unorganized rural society occupying the
plateau'. Similar observations were made for
the Grand-Hinvi block on the Allada plateau
(Vallet and Hurault 1968). When government
interventions involve reorganizing the man-land
relationships, generally speaking the peasant
farmers tend to think 'these plantations are
for the Government' (Moby-Etia 1976). In management strategies based on trees, traditional
societies believe that those who own the trees
own the land. On the other hand, individualism
on the part of the planters 'conforms poorly
or not at all with organized cropping, which
by definition involves constraints... To organize
their time and their activities as they please,
to be able to act freely and individually, such
are their aspirations' (Moby-Etia 1976). The
peasant farmer has his own particular logic for
organizing his work on the basis of techniques,
land and social structures. If development projects refuse to admit or take this fact into
account, they are certain to encounter 'total
indifference on the part of the beneficiary
parties' (Machioudi Dissou 1972), as happened
in certain palm plantations set up in blocks
at great expense.

THE SOUTH-WEST IVORY COAST: IMPLEMENTATION OF A GENERAL STRATEGY

The example of the oil-palm showed the transition from a natural resource strategy to a land-use strategy aimed at increasing production. Until now, land availability was hardly a limiting factor. Difficulties were concerned more with organizing the labour-force and establishing it on a given territory. On the contrary, in the case of the South-West Ivory Coast the concept of a finite space, imposing a maximum limit to potential natural resources, predominates.

To be more precise, this was seen in the land lying between the Cavally River which follows the Liberian frontier, and the Sassandra River, which flows into the Atlantic Ocean about two hundred kilometers further East. In 1972, this area had a native rural population of only 20,000 for more than 18,000 km^2, i.e. a population density of 1.1/km^2.

This is a very uniform natural area with an extraordinarily sparse population; these two facts have for a long time given rise to an open strategy, with little notion of limitations. For the Bakwé people, living inland, especially to the North and East, hunting played an important rôle as a social activity and as a source of food, along with rain-fed rice, the basis of their agriculture. 'Through hunting, the Bakwé economic sphere stretched for tens of kilometers from the village base, without there being a precise territorial limitation between neighbouring villages' (Léna *et al*. 1977). Because of this, the 'traditional living space' was not identified with the cultivated village lands, nor even with a clan's fatherland, but rather 'the whole of the Bakwé forest' (Léna *et al*. 1977). The Krou people, very much in the majority, are grouped near the coast. Although culturally they are very close to the Bakwé people, the main difference is that their activities are mostly connected with the sea. In the Ivory Coast and in Liberia, they have become the major seafaring people of the West Coast of Africa. Their group strategy is not a resource strategy, but an employment strategy, which impels emigration towards Abidjan and even Libreville.

Two openings have been made in this region: one, the port of San Pedro; the other, the roads laid out across the dense forest towards the more populated areas of the Centre-West and the West, which for a long time have been integrated in the national economy. The roads have become channels through which increasing numbers of migrants move from the North and often from the savanna.

Agricultural allotments reminiscent of certain projects of the former Belgian Congo have been set up for these immigrants in the San Pedro hinterland. In 1971, there were no more than 5,000 immigrants as compared to 20,500 native people in the whole area between the Sassandra and Cavally Rivers, from Taï to the Atlantic (Schwartz 1973). In 1975, after a detailed population census, there were almost 10,000 immigrants in the Bakwé district alone. The majority of the newcomers are Baoulé people (56 per cent), followed by Mossi people originating from Upper Volta (15.5 per cent), and Malinké and Bambara peoples originating from Mali. The immigrants from the Sudan savannas are gradually spreading all over the area, setting up villages as they go. The Baoulé people, on the other hand, are spreading out in lines: the tracks that are made are controlled by chiefs of a rank superior to the camp chiefs. New arrivals are placed far away from the preceding camps so as to reserve the land inbetween, which will be filled up as more people arrive. What basically takes place is that everyone can set up his plantation on the very edge of the tracks. A considerable stretch of land is thus reserved.

The tracks opened in the forest to extract timber play a very important rôle in the pioneer phase of the land-use strategy. They have served as axes for getting to the Parc National de Taï (Taï National Park) in the heart of this region. Once the Park limits were reached, the land-use strategy was applied to the empty lands behind the tracks. It was good to follow the tracks in that these linked up the lands most suited for tree-crop plantations. One tactic for reserving the areas which were not immediately used was to stake out the perimeter or the farthest limit of the desired area by clearing the land, or using other methods which would stop any rival claim. The new immigrant society took on an increasingly hierarchical structure as more people arrived. The newcomer could no longer choose his land, but found he was attributed land in exchange for a sort of allegiance.

In the beginning, from within the village, the Bakwé people dealt individually with the immigrants, whose presence brought them certain advantages. However, they soon found themselves in the presence of an organized mass of people who easily outnumbered them, and thus 'immigration was felt more and more as a dispossession' (Léna *et al*. 1977). The Bakwé strategy consisted in spreading out the village population into a great many camps 'at the edge of the tracks, and preferably at a cross-roads' so as to 'block the immigrants' path by maximum land occupation' (Schwartz 1973).

These conflicts, due to an offensive land-use strategy opposing a defensive one, can be explained by the fact that land was needed for growing two cash crops: coffee and cocoa. The desire for land was accentuated since only part of the area was suitable for growing crops with good yields, but the whole area had to be occupied and cultivated in order to discourage rival claimants. The Bakwé villages also participated in cultivating these crops, although they planted cocoa trees on the land cleared for food crops far less systematically than the others. On the whole, their plantations were not nearly as well managed. The Baoulé people are different from the Dioula and the Mossi peoples in that they continue to grow a considerable amount of yams, and their plantations are mainly for cocoa trees. In addition, they are the only people who, often owning plantations in their country of origin, have capital at the outset and can immediately hire workmen. The Mossi people are extremely hard-working; as for the Dioula people, they have developed the tendency towards hierarchism and making the young people work at the profit of their elders.

Consequently, land has become scarce, and the dense forest is quickly being transformed. There is still land left farther West and South, but there, the pioneer front comes against the classified Taï forest, and also the areas which have been earmarked for major agricultural and sylvicultural projects. As in the rest of the Ivory Coast, the family plantation economy, which is so wasteful of land, should evolve towards localized specialization.

Except for the particular case of extracting timber, most of the available land of the South-West is to be developed by specialized State and semi-public companies, and through a vast project for the manufacture of paper-pulp. The State and semi-public companies plan agro-industrial complexes for oil-palms, Para rubber trees and coconut palms. As for the paper-pulp project, it plans to use hundreds of thousands of hectares of ungraded forest, then the tropical pine and eucalyptus forest which will be planted once this has been cut down. The Taï National Park, which will be extended by the Haute-Dodo classified forest to the South must, in the face of this strategy for massive forest and forest soil utilization, protect one of the richest floras of the Ivory Coast forests (one of the refuges for the rain forest during the Quaternary dry periods).

However, the major projects utilizing the forest are likely to find they lack manpower. The agro-industrial projects that are planned at present will need more than 11,000 men by the year 1980: 3,000 are already on the site and 8,000 are still to be found. Immigration from Upper Volta is slowing down, and the 11,000 Kroumen, or supposed Kroumen, are not willing to be employed. In addition, the salaries of the agro-industrial sector are much lower than those of jobs in the cities.

State intervention in South-West Ivory Coast is represented by the Autorité de la Région du Sud-Ouest (ARSO) (South-West Regional Authority), directly attached to the Presidency of the Republic. This body has been assigned very general powers for an area of 36,000 km^2 which goes beyond the area between the Sassandra and Cavally Rivers to the North (up to Guiglo), and also on the left bank of the Sassandra. Both the decisions and impetus fraction arose from a single unit at the highest level, and therefore a two-fold general strategy - in time and space - was elaborated. With respect to time, development under ARSO has three phases: immediately exploiting the forest in order to make the port profitable; creating major agro-industrial projects to provide employment and trade after the timber harvest; setting up viable industries to ensure this region's economic development. With respect to space, the different categories of users are allocated land according to a land-use map which is increasingly detailed and periodically revised. Even medium-size plantations will have their place. The land is divided amongst the native cultivators, immigrant planters, village plantations attached to agro-industrial blocks, the various projects organizing family agriculture (rice, cocoa-coffee, etc.), all of which occupy the areas lying between the large projects. This aspect of future land-use is the most difficult to plan, and as such has been rather neglected in plans for resource management.

IV. CONCLUSIONS

Generally speaking, the strategies used by public authorities to manage the natural resources of the forest zone, its borders, and the moist savannas have had at best, only a limited success. All the same, even when projects have not been executed, or have been carried out differently from what was planned, or else have not proved viable in the long term, the overall results cannot be entirely negative.

In general, most projects appear to be rather costly when considering the profitability of investments in relation to the end results. The same amount of money and skill should have resulted in much more obvious changes. Such poor returns can be explained by three types of difficulties. Firstly, some projects did not fully take into account the possibilities and the limits of the ecological and technical situation. Secondly, many interventions floundered because of a poor financial structure: under-estimation of investments and over-estimation of expected results. Thirdly and lastly, almost all the projects were far too complacent with respect to rural societies, having tended to reduce them to groups of individuals or entities which could be manipulated according to technical requirements. This is probably the most important aspect. Indeed, any disappointments tend to be considered as being the fault of the cultivators who had not done what was expected of them. The cultivators are judged in terms which imply that they lack dynamism and foresight, are inconsistent, and do not really know where their interests lie. They are guilty of not following the supposedly universal logic of the development projects. However, it is too often forgotten that the cultivators taking part in a project can collectively have a coherent attitude towards obtaining or conserving the things they consider essential; and that in order to do this, they are capable of acting in a very complex manner according to the situation in which they find themselves. This therefore means that each rural society has its own rationality, different to that of the developers, inspiring strategies which have to be taken into account.

There are three essential points where the reasoning behind modern strategies differs radically from that of the peasant or traditional strategies. Modern strategy is aimed at increasing assets. In order to obtain this objective, people tend to be reduced (or likened) to their productive capacity and their function in the production system. The objectives of individual strategies and ambitions come directly under the overall objective: material prosperity and social fulfilment overlap so much that they cannot be set apart. Traditional strategies, on the other hand, are essentially social strategies. They aim at making the group as big as possible compared to other groups, and, for the individual, at obtaining maximum power and social status within the group. The individual always acts in society in relation to others, involving them, depending on them, or using them as mediators between himself and others. Some rural societies traditionally and openly consider that money is very important. Well before the colonial era, some peoples – as has been described for the Baoulé and Adioukrou peoples and the societies of the 'Oil River States' – considered that a wealthy man was as such a socially powerful personage. Even in this particular example, material goods are a simple means for reaching a social objective: the control of as many people as possible. This comes back to the strategy of population numbers, as practised in its basic form by the Ngbaka people, described earlier.

Another essential difference between the two types of strategies is the ways and means in which resources are used. Modern strategies try to extract the maximum per unit area; in addition, they endeavour to minimize costs, especially concerning travel and transport, by applying a rational form of land-use. Traditional strategy does not give very much importance to economizing land except when land is scarce owing to high population density (or population concentrated in very large villages). The expeditious techniques of extensive agriculture are preferred as long as there is plenty of land. In a subsistence economy, such techniques, involving the least time and effort, provide the basic food supplies; in a money-based economy, maximum returns for a given amount of work. However, just as for earning money, saving time is not an end in itself. It gives additional scope to the freedom of social action, which itself contains the essential interests. Nothing better illustrates the conflicting objectives of the two strategies than the attitude to growing tree crops in forest areas. The public authorities wanted carefully-grown crops giving high yields; the 'family' planters persist in extending the areas planted, even if it entails neglecting crop maintenance, to the point that cropping becomes a simple gathering activity.

However, the greatest difference between the two strategies is the way in which time and space are perceived. Modern strategy is basically deductive. It fixes definite objectives on a small scale. Localized projects and successive phases are planned through this projection into the future and according to their national importance. This type of process means that time and space are united in a rigid system, where duration is cut up into phases and area into packaged portions. This two-fold division results in development projects composed of a series of stages and with a geometrical lay-out. As for traditional strategies, they sometimes refuse to admit the future, which they try to make as similar as possible to the present. However, in most cases, these strategies really do consider future events. The different levels of society view the future as a project. This involves an inductive process, however, starting from the present situation, and projecting indefinitely into time and space. Duration and area are delimited accordingly when the project is realized.

The difficulties encountered by projects for natural resource management can be explained by these differences. In all cases, to begin with, there is an initiative on the part of the public authorities or an organization duly commissioned by the State. There are then three possible attitudes. The first consists in ignoring, or not taking into account, the fact that the other party has its own set of social rules, or else in proceding as if it were going to act 'rationally' in the sense understood by the decision-makers. This attitude may result in the rural societies taking no further interest in the projects proposed to them. This case is illustrated by the majority of interventions concerning, or based on, existing palm groves. Usually, peasant societies try to use the projects to serve their own interests. This is particularly shown by the fact that crops are constantly grown 'outside the plots' or 'outside the 'paysannats'', etc.; the people having received plots on a developed piece of land thus systematically try to escape from the restrictions of the system imposed on them. The only personal initiative remaining is to be master of an individually cultivated piece of land. Another way in which 'beneficiary members' can 'reap' the advantages of modern strategies consists in only participating for a limited period: the time necessary for saving enough money for developing some land on their own, but very much in relation to their society of origin.

A second attitude amounts to avoiding contact with the rural societies which might hinder the project's progress by mixing in their own objectives. The best way to avoid interference of this kind is to develop land away from populated and cultivated areas. This is why developers prefer wildlands that are free from any social control. The South-West

Ivory Coast, empty compared with other regions, was thus one of the choice areas for development. Elsewhere, projects sometimes have to be content with areas lying within or on the edge of cultivated lands which are neglected by traditional production systems, for example, the flats. Projects in such situations may run into two sorts of difficulties. Firstly, the areas are often more settled than originally thought. It has been seen, for example, in the San Pedro hinterland, that the local societies stubbornly defend the lands where they hunt and gather fruit, etc.

Thirdly, and even more important, any project which calls upon participation from local societies, or even people taken on individually, incorporates different patterns of conduct based on other strategies into its system.

The only solution then is to come to terms with the strategies which inevitably face the project. This is really what developers try to do, as is shown by the sociological studies which are increasingly associated with the preparation of development projects. However, such studies are not always completely impartial Moreover, there has never been a case where sociological considerations have anulled or deferred a development project considered possible from both the technical and financial point of view. Indeed, perhaps it should be questioned whether in principle it is possible to combine the two strategies according to a plan prepared in advance. This amounts to assuming that the two opposing societies with their respective strategies have already come together: on the one hand, the largely standardized modern strategy, based on urban and State principles; and on the other hand, the highly varied, rural traditional strategy. Under the present circumstances, each party tries to take the technical, financial and social resources of the opposing party and divert them to its own interests. Rather than planning everything in detail in advance, it would be better to accept the situation as it is, and admit that it will adjust gradually with time. All that is needed is that initial propositions be reasonable and lie within what is 'feasible' for the villages and peasant farmers (Althabe 1968). Such an open-ended procedure, which can lead to a variety of solutions, obviously excludes obtaining results at all costs in the time and space indicated by a financial programme.

BIBLIOGRAPHY

ALTHABE, G. 1968. Problèmes socio-économiques des communautés villageoises de la Côte orientale malgache. *Tiers-Monde*, 9, p. 129-160.

ANON. *1910-1960. Volume jubilaire du Bulletin agricole du Congo belge.*(Bruxelles).

ANTHEAUME, B. 1972. La palmeraie du Mono : approche géographique. *Cahiers d'études africaines*, 47, p. 458-484.

AUBREVILLE, A. 1948. *Etude sur les forêts de l'Afrique Equatoriale Française et du Cameroun.* Bull. Scientif. N° 2. Section technique d'agriculture tropicale, Nogent-sur-Marne.

BALANDIER, G.; PAUVERT, J.C. 1952. *Les villages gabonais. Aspects démographiques, économiques, sociologiques. Projets de modernisation.* Mémoires Institut d'Etudes centrafricaines, n° 51. Brazzaville.

BEGUIN, H. 1960. *La mise en valeur agricole du sud-est du Kasaï.* Publ. INEAC, Sér. sci., n° 88, 289 p. Bruxelles.

BLANC-PAMARD, C. 1975. *Un jeu écologique différentiel : les communautés rurales du contact forêt-savane au fond du "V Baoulé" (Côte d'Ivoire).* Lab. de Sociologie et de Géographie africaines, Paris.

COÈNE, R. de. 1956. Agricultural settlement in the Belgian Congo. *Tropical Agriculture*, 33, p. 1-12.

DUPIRE, M.; BOUTILLIER, J. 1958. *Le pays Adioukrou et sa palmeraie (Basse Côte d'Ivoire). Etude socio-économique.* L'Homme d'Outre-Mer, n° 4. Office de la recherche scientifique et technique outre-mer (ORSTOM), Paris.

ETIENNE, M.; ETIENNE, P. 1966. L'organisation sociale des Baoulé. In: *Etude régionale de Bouaké 1962-1964. Tome 1 : Le peuplement*, p. 121-158 et 163-167. Ministère du Plan, République de Côte d'Ivoire.

FLOYD, B. 1969. *Eastern Nigeria. A geographical review.* Macmillan, London.

JONES, G.I. 1963. *The trading states of the oil rivers. A study of political development in eastern Nigeria.* Published for the International African Institute by Oxford University Press, London-Ibadan-Accra. (Reprinted 1970).

LASSAILLY, V. 1976. *Espace utile et charge de population dans un des secteurs touchés par la mise en eau du barrage de Kossou (sous-préfecture de Béoumi, Côte d'Ivoire)*, Laboratoire de Sociologie et de Géographie africaines, Paris.

LENA, P.; MARTINET, F.; RICHARD, J.F.; SCHWARTZ, A. 1977. *Le dynamisme pionnier dans le Sud-Ouest ivoirien. Ses effets sur le milieu forestier.* Rapport final d'un projet de recherche du Programme MAB. Office de la recherche scientifique et technique outre-mer (ORSTOM), Abidjan.

MACHIOUDI DISSOU. 1972. Développement et mise en valeur des plantations de palmier à huile au Dahomey. *Cahiers d'études africaines*, 47, p. 485-500.

MOBY-ETIA, P. 1976. *Les pays du bas-Mungo, bas-Wouri. Etude géographique de la vie rurale et des relations avec Douala.* Thèse doctorat 3e cycle, Université de Paris I.

MONDJANNAGNI, A.C. 1969. *Contribution à l'étude des paysages végétaux du bas-Dahomey.* Ann. Univ. Abidjan, série G, vol. 1, fasc. 2.

MONDJANNAGNI, A.C. 1977. *Campagnes et villes au sud de la République Populaire du Bénin.* Agence de Coopération Culturelle et Technique et Mouton, Paris.

MONNIER, Y. 1968. *Les effets des feux de brousse sur une savane préforestière de Côte d'Ivoire.* Etudes Eburnéennes, IX. Abidjan.

MOUTON, J.; SILLANS, R. 1954. Les cultures indigènes dans les régions forestières de l'Oubangui-Chari. *Annales Musée Col. Marseille*, 7e série, 2e vol.

NICOLAI, H. 1963. *Le Kwilu.* Centre scientifique et médical de l'Université libre de Bruxelles en Afrique centrale (CEMUBAC), Bruxelles.

PÉLISSIER, P. 1963. *Les pays du Bas-Ouémé. Une région témoin du Dahomey méridional.* Université de Dakar, Faculté des lettres et sciences humaines, Dépt. de Géographie.

PILLET-SCHWARTZ, A.M. 1973. *Capitalisme d'Etat et développement rural en Côte d'Ivoire. La Société pour le Développement et l'Exploitation du Palmier à Huile en pays ébrié.* Ecole pratique des Hautes Etudes et Centre national de la recherche scientifique, Paris.

RIPAILLES, C. 1966. Les activités et la production agricoles : le secteur primaire. In: *Etude régionale de Bouaké 1962-1964. Tome 2 : L'économie*, p. 45-183. Ministère du Plan, République de Côte d'Ivoire.

SALVERTE-MARMIER, P. de; SALVERTE-MARMIER, M.A. de. 1966. Les étapes du peuplement (jusqu'en 1930). In: *Etude régionale de Bouaké 1962-1964. Tome 1 : Le peuplement*, p. 13-57. Ministère du Plan, République de Côte d'Ivoire.

SAUTTER, G. 1966. *De l'Atlantique au fleuve Congo, une géographie du sous-peuplement.* Mouton, Paris.

SCHWARTZ, A. 1973. *Peuplement autochtone et immigration dans le Sud-Ouest ivoirien.* Autorité pour l'Aménagement de la Région du Sud-Ouest et Office de la recherche scientifique et technique outre-mer (ORSTOM), Abidjan.

SCHWARTZ, A. 1976. *La problématique de la main-d'oeuvre dans le Sud-Ouest ivoirien et le projet pâte à papier. Bilan et perspectives.* Centre de Petit-Bassam, Office de la recherche scientifique et technique outre-mer (ORSTOM), Abidjan.

SEVY, G.V. 1972. *Terre Ngbaka. Etude des aspects de la culture matérielle d'une population forestière de la République centrafricaine.* Langues et civilisations à tradition orale, 2. Société pour l'étude des langues africaines (SELAF), Paris.

SMET, R.E. de; HUYSECOM-WOLTER, C. 1972. *Enquête de Fuladu, 1959 : l'emploi du temps du paysan dans un village Sande du Nord-Est du Zaïre.* Centre scientifique et médical de l'Université libre de Bruxelles en Afrique centrale (CEMUBAC), Bruxelles.

SPICHIGER, R.; BLANC-PAMARD, C. 1973. Recherches sur le contact forêt-savane en Côte d'Ivoire : étude du recrû forestier sur des parcelles cultivées en lisière d'un îlot forestier dans le sud du pays baoulé. *Candollea*, 28, p. 21-37.

STANER, P. 1955. Les Paysannats indigènes du Congo belge et du Ruanda-Urundi. *Bull. Agric. Congo belge*, 46, p. 457-558.

THOMAS, J.M.C. 1973. *Les Ngbaka de la Lobaye. Le dépeu-
plement rural chez une population forestière de la
République centrafricaine*. Mouton, Paris-La Haye.

TJEEGA, P. 1974. *Les types d'exploitation du palmier à
huile dans la région d'Eseka (Cameroun)*. Thèse
doctorat 3e cycle, Université de Paris I.

TROUCHAUD, J.P. 1966. L'implantation actuelle de la
population. In: *Etude régionale de Bouaké 1962-1964.
Tome 1 : Le peuplement*, p. 83-120. Ministère du Plan,
République de Côte d'Ivoire.

TULIPPE, O. 1955. Les Paysannats indigènes au Kasaï.
Bull. Soc. belge d'Etudes géographiques, 24, p. 22-57.

VALLET, J.; HURAULT, J. 1968. *Région du Grand Hinvi.
Etude de géographie agraire*. Institut géographique
national, Paris.

WURTZ, J. 1971. *Adiamprikofikro-Douakandro (Côte
d'Ivoire)*. Atlas des structures agraires, N° 5.
Mouton, Paris.

Conclusion

The traditional strategies of African peoples have been fashioned by a long history and varied societies which are usually very dynamic and profoundly restrictive for the individual. It has been noted that these strategies are very varied and highly consistent in themselves, although this is marred by a few contradictions. Modern decision-making, on the other hand, is the strategy of the national authorities for production, co-operative organization, commercialization, transportation, housing, social facilities, etc. It has universally affected these peoples in different ways according to the regions. The case studies, presented by zones, show that the basis and application of decision-making are completely different from traditional strategies: Pélissier and Diarra consider that modern decision-making has rarely had to, or been able to, 'channel traditional strategies to their advantage'; Gallais and Sidikou indicate that this decision-making can be based on new principles 'by involving collective strategies, which are not all traditional in the limited sense of the word'.

These comments were made at the Dakar Seminar by scientists and decision-makers who regretted the profound disparity between traditional strategies and modern strategies. If it is admitted that nothing can be definitely accomplished without the consent and the collaboration of the interested parties, is not the decision-makers' essential problem that of making their decision accepted, shared and integrated into the strategy of the local populations? This then becomes a collective strategy, i.e. a traditional strategy incorporating a greater or lesser amount of decision-making from the outside.

Is such integration possible? At the end of each case study, the conclusion is that decision-makers' strategies clash with traditional strategies. The latter tend to conserve a particular type of society, amounting to,

in effect, a 'choice of society'. The selected society is maintained by the beneficiary parties and individuals and includes the internal social tensions which must eventually be taken into account. However, it shows that people intend to act as a social entity, as indicated by collective activities. Modern decision-making is usually technical or economic in nature, sometimes with a very limited scope, such as, for example, the development of one particular crop. In doing this, it upsets one of the features of the traditional way of life, namely how time is organized. The requirements of the new activities compete, and eventually displace, break up or reduce the other social or productive activities. In addition, it affects the way in which people organize their very existence, and also their social relations and habits. Many decisions which have been described as concerning only one single activity have a much larger impact, however. In the example of the Opération arachide-mil (Groundnut-Millet Project) in Senegal, or the Plan de développement de l'élevage dans la Région de Mopti (Plan for Developing Stock-Raising in the Mopti Region), the purely productive interventions are associated with co-operative type organization and training. The establishments which intervene on a regional scale have a multi-purpose strategy. The Opération des 30 000 ha (30,000 ha Project) in the Senegal delta tries to replace one human context by another; in encouraging the mountain people of North Cameroun to come down to the plain, it is hoped that the socio-economic and politico-cultural situation will be completely transformed. Regrouping forest peoples, either during the colonial era or since independence, is a socio-political enterprise; the agricultural allotments of the former Belgian Congo are intended to create a new form of peasant farming society. Thus most modern decision-making aims from the outset to alter social structures somewhat. The apparent difference between the ambitions of modern and traditional strategies should be described as it really is: possible conflict between two visions of society. This is the reason why traditional societies clearly realize that decision-making which apparently concerns only techniques, represents a threat to their social structure. If the decision is applied, other social bonds, other hierarchies and other leaders will replace the original ones. If a traditional society refuses a development project, it is not because of the economic aspects but the social changes involved; such a refusal is therefore neither behind the times, nor anachronistic, nor incomprehensible.

In the event that the two types of strategies will eventually be integrated, it is necessary that the opposing forces be clearly understood, and that the social consequences of technical decisions be apprehended as completely as possible by analyses and comparative studies. It must be admitted that such analysis is never attempted. It is indispensable, however, for predicting the amount and the level of resistance, as well as the extent to which traditional strategy will divert the decision-makers' actions to its own advantage. Such an analysis is even more useful in that several societies or social tendencies are subjected to the consequences of modern decision-making. A project for developing stock-raising could benefit a village-based, agricultural society rather than a mobile stock-raising society.

Decision-makers can choose one of two solutions to avoid such social difficulties. Firstly, decision-makers who wish to extend a certain model of society choose interventions which are least likely to fail. The programmes for developing plantations of tree crops are a good example of this choice. They were based as much on the traditional practice of growing tree crops as on the ambition and dynamism of a few people who were ready to break away from the collective land-tenure system ruling characteristic of this form of agriculture. This means that a society's community values were condemned without direct confrontation. Owing to the difficulties resulting from population pressure and the shortage of land, traditional societies themselves offer the weak points suitable for introducing new techniques involving social changes. Modern decision-making therefore uses these difficulties to gradually impose the necessary alterations.

The second solution is to place modern decision-making within the social structure of traditional strategies, i.e. to make it easier to apply these strategies by reducing an incidental difficulty or attacking the cause of some trouble; it therefore tries to assist traditional strategy.

Traditional and modern strategies are also different in their degree of flexibility. Nothing is definitely fixed in traditional strategy, neither in time, nor concerning the magnitude of objectives. Collective decisions constantly and more or less successfully adjust situations according to the problems gradually arising from external forces and internal tensions. One of the most important aspects of this readjustment is the flexibility of the land-use system; land is periodically shared out, lent free of charge or hired, thus allowing the constant matching of the area of land cultivated by the family on the basis of the size of the work force. Adjustments are made in time and over small areas. The rationality of traditional strategies owes a great deal to this double basic adaptation in the course of time and in the spatial pattern.

Modern decision-making is generally precise and planned in advance; it fixes its objectives in terms of figures for a series of successive phases, which means that the size of projects and the time necessary to carry them out are rigidly defined. Some projects are carried out more pragmatically and progressively, but in most cases they predict a certain production at the end of a given number of years, a certain size of colonist population, etc. Such precision is neither a guarantee of success nor of a rational intervention, however, since the objectives are rarely reached. The plan can be revised, by deciding to make a break to stabilize the situation and wait before taking the next step, or by suddenly accelerating the programme; but such procedures never involve the immediate responses of the flexible traditional strategy. Such inflexibility means that modern strategy generally does not attend to the adjustments needed at the regional or local levels. It ignores, for example, certain geographical conditions which, once carefully considered, would make it necessary to diversify the basic type of interventions planned for developing a certain crop. Similarly, on the level of the individual farm, the standard cropping areas as fixed by the agronomist come against a changing situation in terms of labour-force and requirements. Modern decision-making cannot be incorporated into a collective strategy unless it plans to take account of the gradual reactions of the society concerned, and of local adaptations as required by public opinion. Each project would then have to include a system for continually observing the general situation, and the data thus obtained would be used to redefine objectives and methods. There are hardly any projects which provide for such observations during their realization. It is not easy to take account of how the environment gradually reacts while keeping to certain objectives, and this is very rarely attempted in natural resource utilization.

However, it must be admitted that traditional strategies lack the prospective and predictive approach which is one of the main features of modern strategies. It is true that rural populations take a number of precautions in the form of insurances over the short- and medium-term: granaries are filled, livestock is considered as a 'savings bank', the stockmen have a system of reciprocal loans, etc. The weather forecasting systems, of which each people has some basic form, must also be considered. In addition, certain ecosystems are protected and exploited according to various rules; on the Central Niger, for example, the fishermen's traditional authorities forbid access to certain parts of the river at fixed times, so as to let wild animals wait there for the floodwaters; they prohibit the use of nets with too fine a mesh, halting any uncontrollable individual initiatives. In this same region, the Foulani people of Macina have a stock-raising code which is both a clever compromise for maintaining social peace between the different groups of stockmen, and a charter for land-use, ensuring that natural resources are exploited rationally. Many more examples could be mentioned proving that traditional strategies manage the available natural resources; however, they do so according to the current situation, which they try to preserve as much as possible in the future.

Modern strategies sometimes take decisions in order to meet a short-term economic objective which could lead to overexploiting the environment and jeopardizing the future. On the other hand, certain modern strategies are planned ahead using data which traditional strategies cannot take into account: rate of population increase, future market demands, creation of a port, construction of a road, etc.

In conclusion, the differences in kind, method, objectives, terms and actions of the two types of strategy could discourage any attempts to integrate or even simply match them, or to bring them together. However, the history of development projects undertaken in West Africa (after the major mechanized and irrigated agricultural enterprises between 1930 and 1935, which was the time of the spread of animal-drawn equipment and small hydro-agricultural developments, then the present period of integrated, multi-purpose development based on co-operatives) shows that they aimed at higher efficiency, but also that modern strategies come more from outside inspiration (rôle of contract companies and development organizations, courses for technicians, specialized literature) than from observing the local environments and carefully examining the traditional strategies. If a modern strategy wishes to encounter, use and redirect a traditional strategy, decision-making must be conceived in social terms, and in relation to a society being on the defensive. Modern strategy must adapt to the constant flexibility of traditional strategies in time and space, even if the former involves long-term planning. Even if it is difficult to make the two strategies complement each other as desired, interventions must be planned on the basis of local and regional conditions; the project must be continually followed so as to alter its course as necessary; and finally, the fixed financial programmes and stages in profitability, which are not always respected in the development projects undertaken, have to be abandoned.

Unesco publications: national distributors (Abridged list)

(B) SC.78/XXIX. 9/A